Recreations

YURI ANDRUKHOVYCH

Recreations

translated and with an introduction
by Marko Pavlyshyn

illustrated by Volodymyr Makarenko

 Canadian Institute of Ukrainian Studies Press
Edmonton   1998   Toronto

Canadian Institute of Ukrainian Studies Press

University of Alberta
Edmonton, Alberta

University of Toronto
Toronto, Ontario

Copyright © 1998 Canadian Institute of Ukrainian Studies
ISBN 1–895571–21–9 (c); 1–895571–24–3 (p)

Canadian Cataloguing in Publication Data

Andrukhovych, Yuri 1960–
  Recreations

Translation of: Rekreatsii
ISBN 1–895571–21–9

I. Pavlyshyn, Marko.   II. Title.

PG3949.1.N37R4213 1997   891.7'934   C97–931625–1

Publication of this volume is made possible in part by a grant from the
Cosbild Club Endowment Fund.

Printed in Canada

Contents

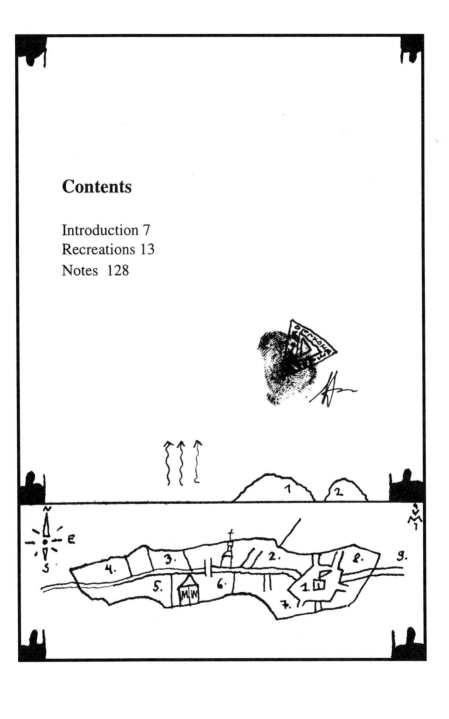

Introduction

Between Chornobyl in April 1986 and the independence referendum of December 1991, Ukraine, like the other constituent republics of the expiring Soviet Union, enjoyed a period of unprecedented political liberalization and cultural excitement. Marvelling at their own audacity, an ever growing cohort of public spokespersons, writers prominent among them, articulated increasingly radical criticisms of the Soviet system and came forward with ever bolder demands. Society mobilized itself. Innumerable informal groups discussed issues of democracy, national rights, ecology, and culture. The cultural elite spoke out in defence of Ukrainian culture, condemning in particular the decline in official support for the Ukrainian language.[1] At demonstrations and marches thousands carried the forbidden blue-and-yellow flag of the Ukrainian People's Republic of 1918–20. Thousands attended festivals celebrating popular culture and youth culture, especially rock music, with a satirical and demonstratively Ukrainian slant. The press carried ever new revelations concerning the crimes of the Soviet past, while journals were packed with the recovered works of banned writers.

In literature, while the attention of the public was fixed most intently upon the rehabilitated literature of the past, new and original voices were beginning to be heard. Critics coined a new collective appellation, "the eightiers," for a generation of poets united by their rejection of ideological prescription. A new wave in Ukrainian prose announced itself in the work of writers of starkly different profiles, yet linked by their common distance from the content and tone of the mainstream. They included Kostiantyn Moskalets, Volodymyr Dibrova, Yevhen (Ievhen) Pashkovsky, Bohdan Zholdak, Halyna Pahutiak, and Yuri (Iurii) Andrukhovych.

Though Andrukhovych had been singled out for praise by the most highly respected novelist of the middle generation of Ukrainian writers, Valerii Shevchuk,[2] he achieved eminence through the publication of *Recreations*. The text appeared in a single issue of *Suchasnist*, a respected journal of literature, culture, society, and politics that had just moved its editorial office from New York to Kyiv. *Recreations* was published in the first issue (1992, no. 1) of that journal that came out in Ukraine— the first that appeared after the independence referendum. The irreverence of the work toward some cherished cultural values, its verbal profanity, and its sexual frankness offended some readers, especially in the Ukrainian diaspora, but the mild scandal certainly did Andrukhovych's public profile no harm. *Recreations* established him as a sophisticated yet seductively readable stylist and, what is more, a major comic writer with penetrating insights into his volatile times.

Yuri Andrukhovych was born on 13 March 1960 in Ivano-Frankivsk in western Ukraine. He graduated from the Ukrainian Institute of Printing in Lviv, served in the Soviet Army in 1983–4 (military life is the theme of seven of his short stories published in 1989),[3] and then worked for a time as an editor for a regional newspaper. His poems began appearing in journals in 1982. His first collection of poetry, *Sky and Squares*, was published in 1985. Subsequent volumes of poetry were *Downtown* (1989) and *Exotic Plants and Flowers* (1991). In 1989–91 Andrukhovych attended courses for young writers from the whole of the Soviet Union in Moscow, an experience upon which he drew in *The Moscoviad (A Horror Novel)*, published in *Suchasnist* in 1993 (nos. 1–2). The novel *Perversion* (*Suchasnist*, 1996, nos. 1–2), set in Venice, continued the satirical and grotesque vein of *Recreations* and *The Moscoviad*. Andrukhovych has been active as a translator, literary critic, and scriptwriter. His essays, especially those in the now all-but-extinct genre of the literary travelogue, are gems of acute observation, elegant generalization, and genial wit.

Much of Andrukhovych's fame is connected to his persona as one of the three members, with Oleksandr Irvanets and Viktor Neborak, of Bu-Ba-Bu, a group of poets specializing in literary happenings, scandals, and provocations. The name of the group, which came together in 1985, comprises the initial syllables of the words "*burlesk*" (burlesque), "*balahan*" (farce) and "*bufonada*" (buffoonery). From its beginning, the group delighted in self-parodic rituals, appointing a Patriarch (Andrukhovych), a Prosecutor (Neborak), and a Bursar (Irvanets). It established a mock Academy of Bu-Ba-Bu and a Bu-Ba-Bu Literary Prize.[4] Never shy of self-promotion, the members of Bu-Ba-Bu commented widely and freely on the nature of their aesthetic project. Andrukhovych, in particular, connected the activity of Bu-Ba-Bu to the rejuvenating role of carnival laughter: "Carnival […] juggles hierarchical values, it turns the world upon its head, it provokes the most sacred ideals in order to rescue them from ossification and death."[5] He saw Bu-Ba-Bu as contributing to the maturation of Ukrainian literature through its "attempt to melt this iceberg of lenten undereducated seriousness that weighs upon everything Ukrainian."[6]

Perhaps the grandest of the Bu-Ba-Bu performances was the staging in the Lviv Opera House over four nights in the autumn of 1992 of the "poetic opera" *Chrysler Imperial*. Andrukhovych later wrote of this extravaganza,

> Nobody—neither the performers, nor the audience—had any idea of what was going on or how it would end. But everyone was delighted, because there was constantly something to be delighted about: if not Shtefko Orobets sporting the ears of Lewis Carroll's Rabbit, then Viktor Morozov as a street bum singing his visceral "Dzhulbars has hanged himself," if not Neborak's flying head, then the hypertrophic male organ of Irvanets (crafted by the artist Marian Savytsky). And in this was expressed the entire nature of Bubabism: its adepts are delighted, im-

mersed up to their ears in the inexplicable joy of existence....

It was a triumph. There was a standing ovation. Certain individuals with droop-
ing moustaches, outraged by this universal blasphemy, angrily left the theatre in
order to write reviews that in some ways were similar to denunciations.[7]

The "poetic opera" celebrated on stage the spirit of carnival that had been announced
in *Recreations*. The motif of the Chrysler Imperial, too, had already made its appearance in the novel as the motor car of the demonic Doctor Popel.

The carnival vitality of *Recreations* makes it a work likely to be enjoyed spon-
taneously by readers without need for special background knowledge. On the other
hand, the text frequently alludes to historical facts not widely known outside Ukraine.
An awareness of these contributes to an understanding especially of the satirical
dimensions of the novel. The central situation—a festival of the "Resurrecting
Spirit"—echoes one of the cultural phenomena most characteristic of Ukraine in
the second half of the 1980s. Mass manifestations of what had but recently been
subculture or counterculture became increasingly frequent and bold. There were
rock and pop music concerts and festivals, including the famous Chervona Ruta
(Red Rue Flower) Festival at Chernivtsi in September 1989, the first of many festivals of that name.[8] The major religious festivals, celebrated openly for the first time
in decades, were accompanied by mass participation in revived folk customs and
rituals. There were also mass events with a more mythological orientation, such as
the Holy Ukraine festival inspired by the science-fiction and fantasy writer Oles
Berdnyk.

While such events occurred in all parts of Ukraine, in the west of the country
they were directly connected to the revival of national sentiment. Western Ukraine,
incorporated into the USSR only after the Second World War, had rather different
experiences in the nineteenth and the first half of the twentieth century than the rest
of the country. Before 1939 the western Ukrainian lands had formed part of Poland.
Before the First World War much of this territory,. including the city of
Andrukhovych's birth, had been part of the Austro-Hungarian Empire. It had ac-
quired a Central European flavour that is often the object of an only slightly ironic
nostalgia in many of Andrukhovych's works. In *Recreations* the city architecture,
the pre-Soviet street names with their Catholic associations, the culture of coffee
and beer, and the multiethnic polite society of Nemyrych's uncanny excursion into
the past are all allusions to a former orientation, not on St. Petersburg or Moscow,
but Vienna.

Hryts Shtundera's nocturnal visit to the now deserted village of his birth relates
to another, more recent, aspect of western Ukrainian history. From 1939 to 1941,
after Hitler's Germany and Stalin's Soviet Union had divided Poland between them,
western Ukraine was joined to the Ukrainian SSR and underwent intense Sovietiza-
tion. This involved the deportation of about half a million people to labour camps in
Siberia and Kazakhstan. After the Nazi occupation and the return of Soviet rule
there were more deportations—again, totalling almost half a million—to Siberia,

Central Asia, and eastern Ukraine.[9] The second of these exoduses forms part of Shtundera's childhood memories.

The figure of Dr. Popel is a reference to yet another fact of Ukrainian life: the diaspora. Ukrainians had been emigrating to various destinations in the western and eastern hemispheres since the late nineteenth century. During the Second World War many were deported to work in the factories and fields of Germany, while others fled the advance of the Soviet Army. Most of those who were not repatriated to the USSR eventually settled in North America, Australia, and South America, but a minority remained in western Europe. Many members of this "Western diaspora," as it came to be called to distinguish it from the millions of Ukrainians dispersed throughout the Soviet Union, were loyal to the idea of an independent Ukraine and maintained the Ukrainian language and culture as best they could in the countries of their settlement. When travel to the USSR became less restricted in the second half of the 1980s, many Ukrainians from the West visited their homeland for the first time since the war years. For all the hospitality that homeland Ukrainians extended to their compatriots, many found their visitors' worldviews, as well as their linguistic and cultural habits, quaint and archaic. The eccentricity that characterizes Dr. Popel in *Recreations* is part of Andrukhovych's benignly satirical commentary upon the diaspora.

Recreations has proved to be a favourite text for literary critics, some of whom have seen it as an example of Ukrainian postmodernism.[10] There are good reasons for this. The book makes light of venerable belief systems and values. Of course, the relics of the Soviet system, as exemplified by the KGB plant Bilynkevych, are contemptible, while its history is sinister in the extreme. But *Recreations* does not promote the obvious alternative—a national ideology in which the nation-state is the supreme good. Indeed, overemphatic national sentiment, represented in *Recreations* (as it had been in fact) by exaggerated regard for national symbols (flags, slogans, patriotic songs, stories about the nation-building heroism of the past), is portrayed satirically. *Recreations* dismisses the cultural habits and judgments of the old colonialism while declining to applaud those of the new anticolonialism. This double refusal has given rise to a view of Andrukhovych as an exemplar of a new post-colonial writing.[11] There is *no* ideological system that can command unreserved and unequivocal respect. Indeed, all values, even the most cherished ones, are but relative.

Perhaps it was the application of this irreverent notion to the ideal of the Poet that gave rise to the greatest ire against *Recreations*. In Ukrainian culture, as in most east European cultures with their heritages of political unfreedom, literature commands reverence as the seat of the conscience of the nation, as a repository of truth and honour in a world defiled by tyranny, and as the trumpet of the ideals of the national community. The force of the symbol of the Poet in such cultures is considerable. Shevchenko in Ukrainian literature, like Mickiewicz in Polish or Pushkin in Russian literature, is practically a sacred figure. The glory of such hero-poets sheds radiance over all who were subsequently anointed members of that noble profession. *Recreations* refuses to reinforce this perception. Martofliak and his colleagues, with their foibles and compromises, are creatures of contingency: not genius but circumstance, social and cultural, makes them what they appear to be.

Parallel to *Recreations'* postmodern scepticism regarding unitary ideologies, values, and myths is its celebration of pleasurable variety. It is here that the carnival quality of the novel is realized. The book rejoices in delighting the reader. For all of its artful devices—its multitude of narrative voices, its second-person narrative, its parodies and allusions—it aims to be lucid, not dark, readable, not forbidding. Echoing Bu-Ba-Bu, *Recreations* delights with its extravagant and eccentric variety. It mixes genres and text types—novella, Gothic horror story, comedy of manners, inner monologue, lyrical verse (including previously published "serious" poems by Andrukhovych himself). It presents a wealth of colourful, piquant, and exotic images, most memorably in the remarkable list of the masks of the carnival procession. It indulges its more sophisticated readers with a feast of literary references, mainly to texts of a similarly carnivalesque profile.

Perhaps the most important such link is to Ivan Kotliarevsky's travestied *Aeneid* (1798–1842), the first modern literary work published in vernacular Ukrainian. (Other connections are remarked upon in the annotations.) Like Andrukhovych's *Recreations*, Kotliarevsky's comic masterpiece brought together for the reader's pleasure numberless acutely and ironically observed details of daily material life. By doing so, in their transitional times both works opened new possibilities for Ukrainian literature. Kotliarevsky discovered the force of a new vision of the Ukrainian people, animated by the wealth and variety of their lifestyle, dignified by their inheritance of Cossack history. It was this vision that gave shape to much of the subsequent culture of anticolonial resistance. Almost two hundred years later, at the very moment of colonialism's death agony, Andrukhovych's *Recreations* showed that even if Ukrainian literature could no longer serve the goal of a distant national liberation, the traditions that it had inherited could be used in other, delightful, ways.

•

I am grateful for the invaluable advice and assistance in this translation of Professor Michael Naydan (Pennsylvania State University) and Roman Senkus (Canadian Institute of Ukrainian Studies).

Marko Pavlyshyn
Melbourne

Notes

[1]   The extent of writers' contributions to Ukrainian national mobilization is made clear in Roman Solchanyk's interview with the poet Pavlo Movchan, "The Beginnings of 'Rukh,'" in Roman Solchanyk, ed., *Ukraine: From Chernobyl' to Sovereignty: A Collection of Interviews* (Edmonton: Canadian Institute of Ukrainian Studies Press, 1992), 7–18. For accounts of various aspects of cultural and literary life of the period, see Marko Pavlyshyn, "Thaws,

Introduction

Literature and the Nationalities Discussion in Ukraine: The Prose of Valerii Shevchuk," in Marko Pavlyshyn, ed., *Glasnost in Context: On the Recurrence of Liberalizations in Central and East European Literatures and Cultures* (New York: Berg, 1990), 49–68; Romana M. Bahry, ed., *Echoes of Glasnost in Soviet Ukraine* (North York, Ont.: Captus, 1990); Solomea Pavlychko, *Letters From Kiev*, trans. Myrna Kostash (Edmonton: Canadian Institute of Ukrainian Studies Press, 1992); and George S. N. Luckyj, "The Era of *Glasnost*, 1987–90," in Dmytro Čyževs'kyj, *A History of Ukrainian Literature*, 2d ed., with George S. N. Luckyj, *An Overview of the Twentieth Century* (New York: Ukrainian Academy of Arts and Sciences; and Englewood, Col.: Ukrainian Academic Press, 1997), 771–6. See also Taras Kuzio and Andrew Wilson, *Ukraine: Perestroika to Independence* (Edmonton and Toronto: Canadian Institute of Ukrainian Studies Press, 1994).

[2] Valerii Shevchuk, "Z vidkrytym zaborolom: Pro prozu Iurii Andrukhovycha," *Prapor*, 1989, no. 7: 101–3, here 103.

[3] One of these has been translated into English by Christine M. Sochocky with George Packer: "Observation Duty," in Ed Hogan, ed., *From Three Worlds: New Ukrainian Writing* (Boston: Zephyr Press, 1996), 207–24 (issue 12 of *Glas*).

[4] For an informed discussion of the avantgardist heritage of Bu-Ba-Bu, Luhosad and Propala hramota, see two articles by Halyna Chernysh: "A ryma dveryma—hup … (Subiektyvni notatky pro deiakykh 'porushnykiv spokoiu' v suchasnii molodii ukrainskii poezii)," *Slovo i chas*, 1990, no. 3: 12–14; and "Semenko brate ia tezh kudlatyi narobym dyva u svita khati," *Prapor*, 1990, no. 7: 22–6. See also Natalka Bilotserkivets, "BU-BA-BU ta in.: Ukrainskyi literaturnyi neoavanhard. Portret odnoho roku," *Slovo i chas*, 1991, no. 1: 42–52; and Oleksandr Hrytsenko, "Avanhard iak tradytsiia," *Prapor*, 1989, no. 7: 156–66.

[5] "'Bu-Ba-Bu' i vse inshe," *Literaturna Ukraina*, 28 March 1991, 7. In an interview with Mykola Riabchuk, Andrukhovych readily acknowledged the affinity between carnival as enacted in the performances of Bu-Ba-Bu and carnival as described by the Russian literary theorist Mikhail Bakhtin (1895–1975). *Suchasnist*, 1992, no. 2: 117.

[6] Iurii Andrukhovych, "Ave, 'Kraisler'!" *Suchasnist* 1994 no. 5: 5–15, here 6.

[7] Ibid., here 12–13.

[8] Romana Bahry, "The Satirical Current in Popular Youth Culture: Rock Music and Film in Ukraine in the 1990s," in Marko Pavlyshyn and J. E. M. Clarke, eds., *Ukraine in the 1990s* (Melbourne: Monash University, Slavic Section, 1992), 146–64.

[9] The deportations are treated in the two most readily available accounts of Ukrainian history in English: Orest Subtelny, *Ukraine: A History* (Toronto: University of Toronto Press, 1988), 456 and 489; and Paul Robert Magosci, *A History of Ukraine* (Toronto: University of Toronto Press, 1996), 619 and 651.

[10] See Tamara Hundorova's article "Postmodernistska fiktsiia Andrukhovycha z postkolonialnym znakom pytannia," *Suchasnist*, 1993, no. 7: 79–83; her observations in "Dekadans i postmodernizm: pytannia movy," *Svito-vyd*, 1995, no. 1 (19): 64–75, here 73; and Slobodanka M. Vladiv-Glover, "Iurii Andrukhovych's *Recreations* and Ukrainian Postmodernism," *Journal of Ukrainian Studies* 20 (1995), nos. 1–2: 79–86.

[11] See my articles, "Shcho peretvoriuietsia v 'Rekreatsiiakh' Andrukhovycha," *Suchasnist*, 1993, no. 12: 115–27; "Post-Colonial Features in Contemporary Ukrainian Culture," *Australian Slavonic and East European Studies* 6 (1992), no. 2: 41–55; and "Ukrainian Literature and the Erotics of Post-Colonialism: Some Modest Propositions," *Harvard Ukrainian Studies* 17 (1993), nos. 1/2: 110–26.

Recreations

LEGEND

= ORG. COM.
ORGANIZING COMMITTEE...

= RESURRECTING SPIRIT

MOON
SUN

1. = Hill no. 1, 2, 3, 4.

forest

church

CHORTOPIL

MARKET SQUARE

ORGANIZING COMMITTEE
ORG. COM.

the WORLD (SKY, EARTH)

PEOPLE, the NATION, the MOB

DRAFT BEER

OSELEDETS (herring)

ОРГКОМІТЕТ - the SAME

OTHER...

For SASHKO and VIKTOR, VIKTOR and SASHKO,[1] without whom this contrivance could never have come to life.

> "Chortopil is surrounded on all sides by mountains."
> (Geographical handbook,
> early twentieth century)

You, Khomsky, or Khoma for short, why, for Pete's sake, are you on this train that left those seemingly interminable plains behind at dusk and, at around half past six, has finally crept into the foothills? Why the hell are you going to Chortopil?[2] More than likely, you'll be of no use to anyone there. You'll be out of place. You've already been getting bored on this train for two days. You've left your pseudo-scholarship at the mercy of the half-wits back home and risk getting booted out of the Institute, but you're going, you're going, because you've been summoned by a telegram signed by Fellini himself, or rather Hitchcock, or rather, no, it's not like that, Hitchcock's telegram probably got lost and instead you've received an invitation to Chortopil to attend this outlandish festival of the Resurrecting Spirit (that, at least, is what it says in the telegram signed "OR-GANIZING COMMITTEE"), arriving no later than May twenty-seventh, hotel accommodation, travel and *per diem* expenses guaranteed, please notify us of your acceptance.

In Lviv[3] you understood that something little short of a pilgrimage was heading for Chortopil. All of the economy-class cars on the train filled up with people anxious to attend the festival, mainly university and senior secondary students, who, the moment the train moved, threw open the windows, stuck countless blue-and-yellow flags[4] out of them, and began singing Sich Riflemen's songs.[5] But you, Khomsky, are no equal for them, you're travelling sleeper-class and you're not certain that anyone is really waiting for you in Chortopil, where that old rogue Matsapura[6] (for who else could have sent that "ORGANIZING COMMITTEE" telegram?) has again taken it into his head to delight the public with a spectacle beyond all prediction.

These first hills aren't very high, and there's no forest but plenty of oil derricks, at the tiny stations they sell home-made wine, guys in embroidered shirts and stone-washed jeans board the economy cars and immediately unfurl the flags they've grabbed for the journey, so it's understood that they, too, are going to Chortopil. Everyone is going to Chortopil. The girls on the whole are unattractive, but they're young, and that's enough, Khomsky. You spend a long time eyeing one of them. For some reason she's not boarding the train, she's still on the platform; the train's about to leave, what's she going to do, she'll miss the festival of the Resurrecting Spirit, dammit, and what will happen then? Khomsky, call out to her before it's too late, tell her to get on, so you call out, Khomsky. The girl smiles, she has too many gold teeth, and suddenly you realize that what you liked best about her were her jeans, so you are not too disappointed when the train pulls out and golden-smiling Marusia remains on the platform after all.

With you in the compartment, Khomsky, is a flamboyant couple—they're Russians or, perhaps, Jews, a pair of romantics risking a holiday in the revolting Carpathian tourist resorts where the corridors smell of carbolic acid and the mineral water of naphtha, but never mind, let them seek their edelweiss in the mountains, he is about sixty-three, she, by the look of things, no more than thirty, which is why yesterday, getting on the train, you decided they were father and daughter and tried to flirt a bit, but the old man cut you quite short, and after that, out of stubbornness and as a matter of principle, you lay in wait for her at the end of the car, pushed her into the W.C., and locking it from inside, began kissing her, she responded, oddly enough, and you kept pressing up against her, pushing her buttocks against the hand basin, Khomsky. You even thought of screwing her right then and there, in the space of two or three minutes, but the train stopped, giving the two of you quite a jolt, you lost your balance and, as you were getting up off the toilet seat, she darted out of the cubicle. After that neither of you said a word to each other.

The fourth seat in the compartment has been empty since Lviv— a retired lieutenant colonel who wasn't going to Chortopil got off there, thank God. He left behind on the shelf copies of *Pravda* and *Red Star*, yesterday he had proposed a few rounds of *durak*,[7] but you, Khomsky, went instead to the dining car, where you ordered dinner and gazed through the window at the gloomy Russian plain.

But here, in our country, it's almost summer, Khomsky, cherry blossoms drift down onto the young grass, the mountains are higher now the farther we go, the forests smell of leaves and spring water, stags bellow, cuckoos call, and at His Eminence's summer residence preparations are almost complete for the season of the great hunt: the floors have been polished, the kilims and the tapestries shaken out, the mirrors and windows washed, delicacies and beverages carted all the way from Vienna, and the family flag raised atop the tower. Soon, very soon, the honoured guests will arrive in their open motorcars, and a huntsmen's band will greet them with trumpets and kettle drums, Khomsky.

There's an hour left to Chortopil, although the train should have arrived there already it's late, all the trains are late now, everything runs behind schedule since "acceleration"[8] was brought in. You are beginning to wonder if all the others will turn up and how Martofliak will look—will he have a beard or not? has he finished his novel in verse? will he bring that little sex-bomb of a wife with him again? After all, sometimes she has to stay behind with the children, and then Martofliak lets go entirely, that is, he gets raving drunk. Of course, there simply won't be any Resurrection of the Spirit unless Martofliak comes. And if he's there, Nemyrych and Hryts will surely be there as well, and only then will it be possible to resurrect anything at all, dammit.

You've never in your life been to Chortopil, Khomsky, though you once had to listen to an angry lecture from the lips of a certain patriotic woman poet about how Chortopil is our spiritual Mecca, it is impossible not to go there if one truly loves one's native land, and all artists must love their native land, Mr. Khomsky, that is what she kept saying for about an hour at the club of the Ukrainian society after occupying the chair next to yours, one and the same thing for an hour with minor variations, holding her face very close to yours so that you could hear her properly, but all you noticed was that she smelled bad, therefore you swore never to go to Chortopil, and yet here you are, Khomsky, you're going, you're going, leaving the institute and Russia to fend for themselves, and Zhenia with her abortion too, you're going a thousand kilometres to spend two days because you have been summoned by a telegram from Matsapura, that genius of an impresario for all epochs and nations.

Just don't let me end up there lonely and unwanted, you pray silently, and what's more the ORGANIZING COMMITTEE is supposed to pay for the round trip and the hotel, and if it doesn't, you'll have to borrow another three hundred from Matsapura, Khomsky, because nothing irritates you more than having to drink at someone else's expense, that's your nature, Khomsky, you pay for your own drinks, and that's it, end of story, I can't stand being obliged to anyone, son of a bitch. Mentally you calculate your earnings for the year—there must be about a thousand by now, but that's peanuts, after all, you're finishing off that novel in short stories and you have a place guaranteed in the 1992 publishing schedule, and therefore forward, Khomsky, life is grand, in the crowded economy cars they are jauntily singing "one, two, one, two, one, two, three,"[9] that's real fascism for you says the husband of your lover from yesterday, but she doesn't know what to say, they're already beginning to regret this trip, why the hell did they have to go to this lair of banditry when the bureau suggested much more interesting and safer destinations, let's say Nagorno-Karabakh or Fergana.[10]

Closer to Chortopil the mountains become lower again and gentler, old guest houses with art nouveau turrets and plaster garden

statuettes of the Pioneers[11] sail past the windows, this is the king-
dom of mineral water and damp sheets in cold rooms, at each stop
the train is besieged by new crowds of pilgrims bound for Chortopil
with their guitars and backpacks, there are even some stooped grand-
pas and grandmas, they've been informed, haven't they, that the
festival will be visited by a bishop—indeed, by no fewer than two
bishops, one from Lviv and the other from Canada, and they will
give their blessings to all who seek them and also consecrate the
wooden Church of the Resurrection in Chortopil, a monument of
the eighteenth century and until recently a storehouse for paper sacks
containing mineral fertilizer, Khomsky.

Well, now, here is the River—great flat stones on its banks, gush-
ing waters, wild garlic on the overhanging cliffs, and now this railway bridge, pretty places, aren't they, says your neighbour to his
faithful little wife, yes, you old Muscovite, life is grand, we are entering Chortopil, our spiritual Mecca, would everyone please get up,
need to check whether I've forgotten anything, manage a farewell
wink to my washroom lover and a quick look at myself in the mirror.

Just right, Khomsky—a long, loose grey coat, a week's stubble
on the chin (Broadway style), hair gathered in a ponytail, sunglasses
circa 1965, a hat, just right, the traveller, rock star, poet, and musician Khomsky, Khoma for short, this cool son of a bitch is bestow-
ing upon provincial Chortopil the joy of a visitation by his very
own person.

From the window at the exit door you watch the railway buildings float by, the station, judging by appearances, dates back to
Austrian days and is festooned with flags and banners, newly arrived festival participants have occupied the platform—they're guz-
zling something or other straight from the bottle, please do not dis-
embark until the train has come to a complete stop, Khomsky,
where's Martofliak, where's Hryts, where's Nemyrych—nothing
but unfamiliar mugs here, some nice girls (and boys) among them,
you step down onto the platform a bit helpless, though you look as
self-assured as an Indian guru—where's Matsapura, damn him, why
the hell did I drag myself here, this festival isn't for me, see the

chicks chattering on their guys' knees, and you, you old goat, you're not wanted here, get out, you miserable imbecile, and at this critical moment you catch sight of a smiling, rosy-cheeked blond ("milk and blood") in an official suit with an "ORGANIZING COMMITTEE" name-tag on his chest holding up in his right hand a cardboard sign inscribed in English: "Mr Khomsky, Leningrad," and your heart grows easy—you are being met, they need you, Khomsky.

Four hours in a bus, even if it's an Icarus,[12] is agony, especially today, when everyone seems to have gone crazy—people are flocking like ravens to Chortopil, the road is choked with cars and buses all sporting flags and heading for Chortopil, it's a collective frenzy, no less, Martofliak is dozing beside me like a baby, he's murmuring softly into his bushy beard, just now he's very like little Ostap, and he doubts whether Ostap is his son, the blockhead, his beard looks as if it's glued on—what a big baby, what a dunderhead, secondgrader in the school of life.

The hope of Ukrainian poetry, Rostyslav Martofliak, thirty, unemployed, father of two children, father of my two children, my husband, Rostyslav Martofliak, leaning toward excess weight and alcoholism, drunkard, rogue, loving father, popular community activist, candidate for parliament, brilliant conversationalist, idolized by women of a certain age, caring son, Rostyslav Martofliak, lover of luxury and hot baths, nighthawk, lounge lizard, dream of all the girls at music school, my biggest baby, egoist and coward, noble knight, gallant cavalier, gentle lover, bland and selfish lover, narcissistic lover, inept lover, golden lover, fantastic lover, sunbeam in my body, O Martofliak!

I would never have come to Chortopil with him if he hadn't insisted. He even gave me an ultimatum: if I didn't go, he'd get dead drunk in Chortopil, shit drunk, raving drunk, drunk day and night, he would drink all he could get, throw up, and drink again until they brought him home all but dead. He knows how to blackmail me, that damned tomcat, I had to go, I had to lie to the children, tell them I was coming back in half an hour, now my heart

races every time I think of my little one—he looked at me as if he understood everything, but I really had to lie to them and go, because this freak, this turd would have carried out his threat for certain, he would have got soaked as a pig, why, he's very proud of keeping his word in everything, oh is he indeed, he just carries on about that, really, the only thing he knows how to do is get drunk.

But does he really care so much whether I go? It's not as though he'd be bored without me. There will be legions of itinerant whores of all kinds in Chortopil, of course, whatever else happens, finding a lay at this festival of the Resurrecting Spirit will be easier than anything else, maybe even easier than finding a bottle, admittedly, he's too narcissistic to go prancing after them, but does he really need me right there? He's so possessive, he scares me a bit, it's seven years since he smashed the china at our wedding, and he gets more and more attached to me all the time, he creeps into me, hides inside me, curls up into a little ball like an embryo, and sleeps, sleeps, sleeps—just as he's sleeping here, on the bus, head on my shoulder, my little darling, spineless rag, incapable of picking up your own broads, Rostyslav Martofliak, blossoming genius, boring intellectual, ear bender, heavenly gift, rare diamond, hope of an expiring aristocratic line, a lord deprived of his inheritance, alcoholic maniac, conformist, official poet, scourge of God, tool of the Devil.

The worst of it is that I know in advance exactly what it will be like in Chortopil. That same crowd—Hryts and Nemyrych, and that Casanova Khomsky, Khomo-homo, with their pretensions, the same old jokes, the same old poems, except maybe this clodhopper will read something new, crowds of fans, autographs, one more inane than the next, boozing in the hotel at night, then Hryts will fall asleep at the table, Nemyrych and Khomsky will go off to the ladies, then Pavlo will come crawling in with his compliments and a bottle and we'll prattle on till morning about some infernal rubbish, or about Ukraine, always the same thing, Matsapura will hang around for ages until I can't take it any more and fall asleep, then he'll finally go and Martofliak will begin searching for anything left in the bottles, bashing the crockery, setting the bathroom agurgle, smoking, finally he'll lie down beside me and we'll make love for five minutes, then he'll fall asleep and three hours later we'll have to get up, the festival program is packed and everyone wants Martofliak, head splitting, eyes red, oh, how familiar all this is, how tedious these festivals, this Resurrection of the Spirit, this vacuum ...

Actually, they're talented boys, honest, not mercenary, flower of the nation, children of the new age, thirty-year-old poets, each imagines he's the centre of the universe, but really it's only their sexual frustration and feverish egomania—I can read them like a book—nervous movements, eyes shining, every miniskirt the source of inner tempests, the legs as such don't matter, anyway what do they know about legs, all their fantasies about women are twisted and pathological, treatment is what they need, particularly Khomsky with his queer deviations, Khomo-homo, he got dressed up as a hooker for Oleksa's birthday party, put on make-up, flashed his thighs in fishnet stockings, danced a tango with Nemyrych, then announced he was going to do a striptease and, gyrating to some endless disco tune, began to undress, the interesting thing was that he really did have a bra on, I was on the point of closing my eyes because that idiot really might have stripped naked, but instead he pulled that thing out of his panties, a rubber one admittedly, someone had brought it back for him from the States, it was full of water and he began squirting everybody with it, then he threw it to the girls, who just about fainted from overexcitement, the moron.

Sleep in peace, Martofliak, husband of mine, till we get to Chortopil, we'll have a great time there, at least half an hour to go yet, I often came here as a child with my parents, I practically know the road by heart, there's Painted Rock coming into view already, then comes the aqueduct, ancient Roman, they say, then "The Hut," unventilated and reeking of kabob, then Lanckoroński's Gothic villa, now a museum (what blackberries on those slopes, the most abundant I've seen), sleep in peace, the mountains will save us, we'll live another hundred years and then die on the same day,[13] because otherwise you won't cope, you'll drink yourself to death—in the next world or this one, it doesn't matter, you'd find booze anywhere, I know you, it's a blood-substitute for you, there's alcohol pulsing in your veins, it makes you feel warm and cozy, you feel like you're rocking in the clouds, cut your finger and there's vodka instead of blood, that's quite normal, it's in your genes, you can't be any different, with another woman you'd have hanged yourself long ago, but you're lucky, you fool, that I'm me and not somebody else, my lord, my master, my beloved spouse.

You always shudder in your sleep for no reason, sometimes you shout, and just now you've twitched like a madman, he's always dreaming about some abomination or other, but he almost never remembers what, so why are you staring at us, boy, do I still appeal to twenty-year-olds, he's looking at me, he's openly eyeing me, what a nice boy, thin, embroidered shirt and jeans, golden hair, deep-set eyes, slim as a god. But this is too much, mister, I'm travelling with my husband, am I not, and though he's asleep, he's right next to me. Take these seven years away and maybe I'd play this game of looks and eyes and hints with you, because you're a very pretty boy, likely a student, you haven't got a seat, poor thing, standing in the aisle, you're bored so you stare at married women, a young Don Juan, a sprite, a reed, a veritable flute, you've probably left the Komsomol[14] and joined SNUM[15] and Lord knows what else, there's your red-and-black badge[16] right where it should be and a David Bowie haircut, a playboy in the making, what a delicate little thing, probably shaves no more than once a fortnight, Martofliak was like that too when we first met, really, this is too much, why are you coming over here, we're travelling together, can't you see, the funny thing is that Martofliak won't wake up, he won't even be jealous, he's dreaming some horror again—decrepit old men in rags, leprous monks, swamps, a black dog with snarling bloody jaws, that kind of thing, well, what are you going to say now that you've come up to me, say something, don't smile like an imbecile, I can smile too, even quite enticingly …

"Excuse me, is that Mr. Martofliak?"

So that's it! He's recognized my husband! And I, stupid old nitwit, I believed your eyes—after all, that's the way men look at women. Well, now he'll ask for an autograph and express his admiration—it's a good thing we're nearly there, the first of the Chortopil villas has just appeared in the window: wild grapes, stone walls, flags atop the towers, and mountains overhanging the narrow streets.

Yes, boy, that's him, that's Rostyslav Martofliak whom you hold in such esteem, you're a real fan of my husband's, so you should at least kiss the hand of the woman who washes your idol's socks and makes soup for him and doesn't sleep when he's out till morning, drunk in the company of dubious politicians and businessmen, and then, while he sleeps in all day, she nods off at work and runs to fetch the kids from day care in the hope of finding him at home in the evening, but he's gone again, because he has to squander the last kopek of the honorarium that he has hidden from you, and you revere him like a saint, you poor boy.

"Mr. Martofliak is going to recite his poems at the festival of the Resurrecting Spirit?"

Of course he is, what else would he do if he failed to read his brilliant poems, that would be a national tragedy or worse—to be in Chortopil and not to flatter his self-esteem through public masturbation, reading his poems or a piece from that novel in verse, which, believe me, he's never going to finish, I know him, but in the meantime he'll puff up his cheeks and strut about like a peacock to thunderous applause, the flowers he'll pass on to me, he's so brilliant and irresistible with that bushy beard of his.

So, you're satisfied, boy, you may go, don't forget to buy a ticket to the poetry evening, otherwise you won't get high on my husband, this sleeping prophet, still snoring gently although we're already turning into the bus station, God, what a lot of buses, time to wake him, it's quarter to eight, at eight we're supposed to meet everybody at Market Square and he's still asleep, miserable sack, bag of shit, oracle, future of the nation, empty jug, scarecrow, joy of mine, father of my children, pleasure of my body, my conqueror, my miracle, my eternal orgasm, we've arrived, out you go, Rostyk.

Driving a prewar Chrysler Imperial along a mountain highway is a great pleasure. One can confidently overtake this whole Soviet motorized river that's flowing toward Chortopil, tear ahead, take the lead, and be the first to arrive at the festival. You feel like a Chicago gangster in the thirties whom solicitous guardians are taking for a holiday somewhere on the Riviera to wipe out quietly in one of the luxury hotels. This thought makes you warm and uneasy.

Hryts Shtundera and Yurko Nemyrych had been trying to hitch a ride at the Kolomyia on-ramp for almost an hour, but no swine would stop to give them a lift, though everyone was headed for Chortopil. And then, when the supply of profanities and cigarettes had been exhausted and the prospect of being late for the festival was increasing as fast as the threat of civil war, an implausible Chrysler Imperial with foreign plates showed up, and a charming, grey-bearded gentleman in a checked cap and a grey travelling suit kindly braked to a halt and invited them to take a seat. His Ukrainian was good though also of prewar vintage, from which Nemyrych immediately concluded that the gentleman in the cap was an émigré.

"I am Popel, Doctor of Medicine, citizen of Switzerland," said the old man once they had set off, "private clinic in Lucerne, canton of Bayonne."[17]

"Shtundera," said Nemyrych.

"Nemyrych," said Shtundera.

"Delighted to travel with such renowned poets." Dr Popel's esteem was dumbfounding.

"You've heard of us?" asked Yurko, who was sitting in the front seat, turning his entire body toward him.

"We know what's happening in Ukraine," said the doctor, as if by way of explanation.

"Then let's have a smoke, because ours have run out," said Hryts, leaning forward from the back seat.

"But of course." And two packets of exceptionally flavourful Gauloise cigarettes surfaced from the magnanimous pocket of Mr.

Popel, hovered for an instant in his right hand, and flew into the perforated pockets of the itinerant poets.

"We'll smoke yours first, get them out," commanded Nemyrych, but Hryts made a rude gesture at him, whereupon each took a smoke from his own pack.

"Mr. Popel, you aren't by any chance a CIA agent?" inquired Yurko.

"I'm a psychiatrist, Mr. Shtundera."

"I'm Nemyrych."

"Oh, I do apologize, Mr. Nemyrych."

"My name's not Misternemyrych, but Nemyrych."

"I apologize once again."

"That's his idea of a joke. Pay no attention to him," said Hryts. "Have you driven this car all the way from Switzerland?"

"Heavens, no. Just from Lviv. I bought it in Lviv."

"Nice car," said Hryts approvingly.

"Thank you, I like it, too. It's a bit old."

"Mr. Popel, do you think you could organize an invitation to Switzerland for us?" asked Yurko.

"There's no real need for that," said the doctor.

"You meant to say, 'There's no real difficulty in that'?" said Hryts, endeavouring to correct him.

"No, I meant to say that you would be better off going to America. I can arrange an invitation for you to America."

"Mr. Popel, this is my second book. I've inscribed it for you," said Yurko bowing.

"Oh, thank you very kindly. *Flight Into Egypt?* Fine title. I've heard about it somewhere. And I've already got your book," he said, turning to Hryts.

"That makes me very happy, because I haven't had a single book published yet."

"Egad! Then the book I have isn't yours?"

"I'm afraid not."

"Then I hope that I'll receive your book in the future."

"Let me give you the manuscript. I have a copy right here. There you are."

"Ah, splendid. Let me make a gift in exchange. Here's ten dollars. It's not too small an amount?"

"I don't think so."

"Mr. Popel, you don't happen to be interested in the location of military plants in our district?" asked Yurko.

"No, actually. Do you have any connection to military plants?"

"None at all."

"I didn't think you did. I'm not interested in these things. I'm just going to Chortopil for the festival of the Resurrecting Spirit. They say it's going to be quite special. Hutsuls[18] in national costume, music, all manner of dances. I like that sort of thing very much. I've got my video camera with me, so I'll be able to film it."

"What's life like in Switzerland?" asked Hryts, interrupting him.

"You know, it is not so easy to give a short answer to that."

"Did you know Hermann Hesse?" asked Yurko.

"I met him when he was already in the wane of his life. We met at baroque music concerts. Hermann liked the early European classics, even more, perhaps, than jazz or Beethoven. That's what he actually used to say: for him real music ended with Beethoven ..."

"What about Freud? Did you know him?"

"Freud? Not personally, but I attended his lectures in Salzburg before the war."

"You must be quite old, Mr. Popel," Hryts deduced.

"I always look younger than I really am."

"And did you know Jung?"

"Listen, I can't know everyone. I knew some students of his. Some of them worked with me in my clinic."

"Amazing! And did you know Joyce?"

"I read him. He made a huge impression upon me in my youth."

"You read him in English?"

"In French, and then a second time in German."

"And do they know a poet by the name of Antonych in Switzerland?"

"Malkovych?"

"No, Antonych, Bohdan-Ihor Antonych, a poet."[19]

"You know, this is the first time I've heard of him, but I'll certainly look out for his books. Is he a friend of yours?"

"Yes. He's twenty-seven."

"Oh, still very young. That's probably why I don't know him.

"Hryts, why are you so quiet? Are you asleep?" asked Yurko, looking around.

But Hryts was not asleep. He was opening a can of beer which he had come across in the back of the Chrysler.

"I do apologize, I forgot to offer you some," said the doctor, producing another can and handing it to Yurko. "Bavarian. Perhaps you'd like a snack? I've got some ham and Emmenthaler cheese sandwiches, some chips, crackers, tomato paste, salami, orange juice ... Do help yourselves, it's all there on the back seat in those paper bags."

"Very nice. And you're carting this all the way from Switzerland?" Hryts asked after a pause, chewing and swallowing a slice of unbelievably tender, rosy ham.

"Good heavens, no. My family in Lviv packed this for me. They say there's nothing to eat in Chortopil."

"You've got a nice family," concluded Nemyrych. "Are you staying at a hotel in Chortopil?"

"I have family in Chortopil as well. I'll probably stay with them. I think, though, they've all died."

"I see. Have a look at that picturesque crag overhanging the road," said Hryts.

"Painted Rock," said the doctor, quite correctly.

"Right! So you know these places?" Yurko raised his eyebrows.

"I was born here."

"So that's it! Then you must know where to find Market Square in Chortopil," Hryts speculated.

"How could I fail to, I spent my childhood there. My father had a pharmacy on Market Square. I used to play in the back rooms, which were full of boxes of medications, retorts with strange multicoloured fluids, old scales, sea shells, dried exotic plants collected in the mountains in summer, astrolabes, salamanders and

serpents bottled in spirits, silver rings, books in Latin, thermometers ... I'd creep to the very bottom of this world, where all was quiet and peaceful, and listen for the bell at the entrance door. Customers would enter, and I would hear my father talking to them. Generally they were simple Hutsuls who knew nothing about the pharmacopoeia. Later I would hear the town-hall clock strike the next quarter, and I dreamt of staying all my life in those rooms full of scales and bronze candlesticks, hot-water bottles, enemas, syringes ..."

"Condoms," Nemyrych interrupted suddenly.

"I don't remember whether there were condoms," shrugged Dr. Popel. "The Hutsuls probably didn't use them. Do you have problems with condoms?"

"In so far as we are going to the festival of the Resurrecting Spirit, we do," Shtundera said frankly. "There are, you know, going to be lots of pretty girls there whom we have yet to meet."

"Oh, then do, please, help yourselves." And from that magic pocket two neatly packaged rubbers appeared. "That's not a problem."

"What would we do without you, Mr. Popel?" said Nemyrych, showing a friendly set of teeth. "But to return to Market Square. Could you drive us there direct? We're meeting friends there at eight."

"With pleasure, boys."

"We'd like to invite you to the poetry evening tomorrow. We'll be reciting our works," said Hryts, filling his pockets with sandwiches and crackers from the paper bags.

"With pleasure. Thanks for the invitation. Delighted."

After passing the aqueduct and, immediately following, the roadside café called "The Hut," the Chrysler took the final curve into Chortopil quite smoothly considering its condition, and a few minutes later Lanckoroński's Gothic villa appeared on a slope to the right.

"I don't know about nowadays," said Popel after a pause in the conversation, "but in my day there used to be magnificent blackberries over there, behind the Lanckorońskis'. I used to pick them as a boy. I had my first time with a lady there."

"Did you bang her?" Yurko inquired.

"I beg your pardon?"

"He is asking whether sexual intercourse took place," explained Hryts.

"Oh, you want to know that as well! She was a bit bucktoothed."

"And that stopped you?" asked Yurko empathetically.

"No, but to be quite honest, I wasn't in love with her."

"And what is your attitude to women in general?" asked Hryts sagaciously.

"I prefer to keep my relations with them on a purely business footing, as they say here. Women have great powers in this life. Oh, here's Chortopil already! You have no idea what Chortopil means to me! These ancient villas overgrown with wild grapevines, these stone walls, these turrets with their little windows, these mountains that you can see wherever you are, this Dominican church. In a moment, unless I'm mistaken, if we go straight along this street and then turn right, we'll be at Market Square. No, I beg your pardon, it's the second turn to the right, the first leads to the Church of the Resurrection."

"Mr. Popel, you have a superb memory," said Hryts.

"How old are you?" asked Yurko, coming to the point.

"I am not young and I am not old, boys. I am eternal. As, by the way, you are too. Market Square, if you please! Are those people waiting for you? I am sure we'll meet again. Most grateful for your company, it was a pleasure, have a good time!"

"Have a good time, old codger," said Nemyrych, when the majestic Imperial had driven away. Then he looked around.

On the square the final preparations for the festival were in progress: people were bringing out tables, pitching tents, and erecting stages decorated with streamers, garlands, and lanterns. Throngs of people were already arriving with candles, masks, and flags.

"There they are, waiting for us," said Hryts, nodding toward the monument to the founders of the Komsomol looming in the middle of the square. "Look, Martofliak has hauled his wife along again.

Khoma is unrecognizable, as always. But who's that blond-haired swine with them?"

Bilynkevych, for such was the name of the blond-haired swine, worked as an instructor for the Chortopil Komsomol City Committee and was the ORGANIZING COMMITTEE member who had met Khomsky at the station. An officious-looking youth wearing a Soviet-made suit and a tie, almost buoyant in his bearing, he was urging everyone to check immediately into the Blue Mountain Hotel, where, he said, places had been reserved for festival participants. But the company wouldn't even listen to him since Nemyrych's tempestuous brain had given shape to the notion of beer.

"We can't just go without trying the local beer," proclaimed Yurko. "That would be tantamount to eternal dishonour, to ignominious surrender, to showing our back to the enemy, to self-betrayal, to filling our pants. We do, after all, have certain moral obligations toward ourselves!"

The others expressed warm support, except Marta, who made a face, but, as her precious Martofliak had energetically approved Nemyrych's idea, she gave in and set off after the amigos for the wide-open hospitality of "Under the Sign of the Herring," a tavern located right there on Market Square in the cellar of one of the old merchant houses.

After reaching the bottom of a steep and slippery staircase and pushing their way through a smoke-filled jungle of drinkers, who at this hour were more numerous in the bar than usual and of whom not one neglected feeling Marta all over with a damp sticky leer, the company somehow found an empty, foam-stained table. Bilynkevych disappeared into the labyrinths of the kitchen but returned shortly afterwards, and no fewer than two waiters began carrying beer and pretzels to their table. The beer turned out to be good, and Nemyrych recounted its long prehistory, which had its beginnings in the Austrian days, when the famous brewer Machalski established a branch in Chortopil to take advantage of the singularly favourable chemical composition of the water in the River. His calculations proved so apt that before long Chortopil beer was being delivered to the court of His Imperial and Royal Majesty in Vienna.

"This is an extraordinarily instructive story, dear Nemyrych," said Khomsky, "but I'd prefer to hear a little more about the fandango that is soon to take place here. What can you tell us, youthful angel?"

Bilynkevych blushed on being thus addressed, but, understanding that he was dealing with bohemia, pulled himself together and explained:

"The Festival of the Resurrecting Spirit."

"Splendid, young man! You have told us what we know already. I am delighted with this reply."

Everyone laughed, or, more precisely, roared with laughter, but here Bilynkevych experienced the flash of a saving idea, searched through all his pockets, and finally produced from a man's purse vulgarly known as a "pederasticase" a brochure, folded in four, that had been offset printed on paper so beautiful that it must have come from Finland.

"It's all written here," he murmured.

"And where is Matsapura, what is he up to and why didn't he meet us?" the demanding Khomsky further inquired.

"Pavlo Avramovych is very busy as director-in-chief of the festival," Bilynkevych replied readily. "He is occupied with the final rehearsals and preparations, and has delegated to me all matters concerning your accommodation and further participation in the festival. According to our schedule you now have some free time. The festival itself will begin here, on the square, about four hours from now, between midnight and one a.m."

"Listen, this is interesting," interrupted Martofliak in his rich theatrical voice, having previously leafed through the festival brochure in silence. He began reading aloud:

HONOURED CITIZENS, FELLOW COUNTRYMEN, LADIES AND GENTLEMEN!

We have lived to see the day when the dark forces of evil and reaction, challenged by the Luminous Cossack Spirit, tremble in fear! We have been granted a decisive opportunity to prove to ourselves and to the whole civilized world from what noble Forebears we are descended and whose hot Blood courses in our veins. At this time we experience the profound need for a festival that will unite us in a shared impulse to create and to build. Ancient and eternal, like our long-suffering history itself, Chortopil hospitably invites all revellers. The Spirit must be resurrected!

The veritable essence of our masque is triumph over Death. This was well understood by our ancestors, the glorious Zaporozhian Cossacks,[20] studiosi, clerics, and burghers, when each year at the end of May (this fabulous month of Nature Awakened upon our earth, of green paradisiacal proliferation) they conducted their recreations[21]—carnivalesque folk masquerades with singing, dancing, poetry recitations, and theatrical performances. Emancipated souls celebrated their renewal, Free Laughter and Untrammelled Poetry ascended to waft over the sinful earth, and the dastardly Skeletal One retreated before the implacable blows of Human immortality.

On 27–28 May such recreations will be held in Chortopil for the first time in two hundred years and thereby returned to the People under the general title of a "Festival of the Resurrecting Spirit." This festival will become the first step in the rebirth of the ancient and beautiful traditions of our people. We invite everyone to Chortopil!

THE FESTIVAL PROGRAM INCLUDES:

1. *"The Festival That is Forever With Us" a scholarly and theoretical conference. (Papers and other contributions by eminent philosophers, philologists, economists, ecumenists, para- and psychologists, historiosophists, astrologers, political scientists, parliamentarians, hypnotists, demiurges, and others.) 27 May, Great Hall of the City Committee of the Communist Party of Ukraine* **16:00 hours**

2. *Solemn liturgy and reconsecration of the Church of the Resurrection, monument of eighteenth-century wooden architecture. 27 May, Church of the Resurrection in Chortopil* **19:00 hours**

3. *Performance by the folkloric ensemble "The Golden Jews'-Harpists" of the Chortopil District House of Culture. 27 May, auditorium of the "Russia" cinema* **20:00 hours**

4. *Ballroom dancing contest. 27 May, auditorium of the "Russia" cinema* **20:00 hours**

5. *Screening of the art film "Emmanuelle IV" (French). 27 May, auditorium of the "Russia" cinema* **20:00 hours**

6. **00:00 hours**, *28 May: start of carnivalesque masquerade at Market Square, Chortopil. Procession of masks, clown show, fire-eating competition, joke-telling contest, "The Spirit that Spurs the Flesh to Struggle" (oratorio), election of Supermiss, the Festival Queen, tugs-of-war, acrobatic exercises, apocryphal entertainments, theatrical performance of the mystery play "Where Love for Homeland is Heroic,"[22] dancing, tricks, erotic encounters.*

7. *Festive market at Market Square and adjacent to the Church of the Resurrection. 28 May* **from 10:00 hours**

8. *Religious procession to Painted Rock with ascent to the summit. 28 May, columns form at the start of Dzerzhinsky Street* **13:00 hours**

9. *"Presentation of the Corpse" rock festival (performances by Doctor Tahabat,[23] Broken Eggs, Leviathan, Orgasm, Little Fir-Tree, and others). 28 May, environs of Painted Rock* **15:00 hours**

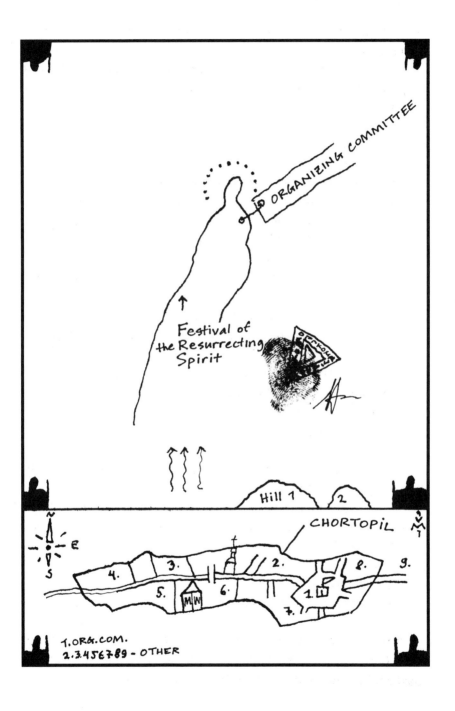

ORGANIZING COMMITTEE

Festival of
the Resurrecting
Spirit

Hill 1   2

CHORTOPIL

4.   3.   2.   8.   9.

5. M W 6.   1.

7.

1.ORG.COM.
2.3.456789 - OTHER

10. *"We Are, Because We Cannot Be," poetry recital, Chortopil City Stadium. 28 May*   **20:00 hours**

11. *Closing notes of the Festival: solemn protest meeting and ritual banquet on the slopes above the River, cleansing of bodies, Great Bonfires.*

The Festival program may contain surprises.

FRIENDS! The Resurrection of our Spirit, and thereby our ultimate liberation, is becoming a reality. We can triumph, and we will triumph! Rejoice and ye shall be joyful!
Glory to Ukraine!

ORGANIZING COMMITTEE

Festival producer and director-in-chief: Pavlo MATSAPURA.
Artistic directors: KAUFMANN-and-KOCH[24]

The Organizing Committee expresses its sincere thanks and profound devotion to the festival sponsors: the Metallica co-operative association (Chortopil), the Intersex joint venture enterprise, and Mr. Franko Popel (Switzerland).

"Now what do you say to all that, friends?" said Martofliak, surveying them with a querying look.

The friends, who were wetting their whiskers in what was, on average, their second tankard, replied approximately as follows:

"Not bad!"

"Crazy!"

"Loony bin!"

"Your Matsapura has finally gone schizoid, I think," concluded Martofliak's Marta.

Yet all these responses signified nothing but joyous approval, and Martofliak remained satisfied with the effect that his rich and masterful reading had exercised upon the audience.

"Hryts and I can tell you even more. Mr. Popel from Switzerland, mentioned as a sponsor, is a good friend of ours. On the way here he presented us with a condom each and promised to invite us to the States," said Nemyrych informatively.

"Really?" Marta's interest was aroused.

"Don't get excited, Marta dear, we'll definitely take your husband along. À propos, you look enchanting today," said Nemyrych, wetly kissing her hand.

Marta enjoyed this, but didn't let on:

"My husband already has an invitation to America."

"Bring me back a toy prick from there, old buddy," begged Khomsky. "Remember, I had one of those once. You fill them up with warm water. Trouble is, some creep stole it, probably from the hostel."

"A girl, no doubt," guessed Martofliak,

"And do you still have your own?" asked Hryts and Nemyrych almost simultaneously.

"That would be easy to ascertain, boys," replied Khoma, condescendingly. "We'll go to bed together today and you'll find out."

"I'm afraid we won't get to bed at all, given the fullness of the program," said Martofliak, deflecting the conversation from a topic that was embarrassing Marta.

"If that's the case, why did we bother coming—and, what's more, why did we waste our time getting condoms?" asked Hryts, indignant.

"Is anyone asking you to hang out at the festival for the entire time?" said Khomsky. "Find yourself some supermiss or other and take off! We're all free to choose. Captives can't create an unfettered carnival. If you want to be free, be free."

"I absolutely agree with Khoma," pronounced Martofliak sagely, but immediately came up against a sharp look from Marta.

"In what sense?" she inquired.

"In the sense that if I want to get drunk I'll get drunk, and that's all there is to it!"

"Don't be rude to your wife, old man, she's simply fantastic today," intervened Khomsky charitably, and kissed Marta on the cheek.

In the meantime Bilynkevych, aware that he had been entrusted with looking after major contemporary poets, and aware that he was, indeed, looking after them, had no idea how to react to this fairly explicit banter, and for that reason felt somewhat out of place. He did, admittedly, try to smile and knowingly nodded his head, which, however, was beginning to ache a bit—perhaps from the luxurious Chortopil beer, to which the youthful Komsomol chieftain was unaccustomed, or perhaps from the excessive tobacco smoke, which was etching out his eyes. Taking advantage of a momentary pause in the convivial chit-chat, Bilynkevych sought to clarify an issue that, apparently, had long given him no peace:

"You don't happen to know what the poet Mykola Nahnybida[25] is working on at the moment?"

"You know, old man, I believe he died some thirty years ago," Nemyrych obligingly explained. "It is, however, altogether possible that he's working on something, though up till now there has been no news of him."

"Died?" asked Bilynkevych, genuinely shocked. "But he gave some readings here only last year! I attended his lecture at the House of Culture."

"What you have just said, Ivan, may absolutely have taken place. In a certain sense the poet Mykola Nahnybida is eternally alive and omnipresent, like Krishna," Yurko tolerantly responded.

Not fully satisfied, Bilynkevych continued the literary discussion:

"Later he dined at the Marketplace Restaurant, here, next to the tavern. He ordered a Hutsul schnitzel. And he ate it."

"So, if I've understood you correctly, you believe that this was not a ghost, but a completely earthly man of flesh and lymph?" said Nemyrych.

"Well, yes."

"Perhaps you've confused him with some other great poet?"

"How could I? I personally reserved a room for him at the hotel!"

"Then it must have been some other Nahnybida who's also a poet," speculated Hryts.

"Exactly!" said Bilynkevych, relieved. "That must be it."

And here he posed a new question that must have been of importance to him:

"Is it true that the writer Kostiuchenko was run over in Kyiv by a car, a black Volga, and that he's now in intensive care?"

Marta whispered something in her husband's ear.

"Go by yourself," he replied aloud.

"Can you believe that!" Marta was offended. "With those drunken sots over there?"

"They won't eat you," intoned Martofliak gloomily.

"Marta, perhaps at least on this occasion I may substitute for your husband," said Khomsky, offering his hand.

"Swine," said Marta over the head of the immovable Martofliak, and rose to follow Khomsky.

Two paces away they dissolved into the cigarette smoke and the thick hubbub of the tavern.

"It's not true that Kostiuchenko was run over," said Nemyrych, continuing the question-and-answer session. "As late as yesterday afternoon he was drinking coffee with me in the Aeneas Restaurant."[26]

"You're personally acquainted with the writer Kostiuchenko?" asked Bilynkevych, visibly brightening up.

"I've hauled him home drunk in a taxi a few times. That's as far as the acquaintance went," yawned Nemyrych.

"Then perhaps you also know the writer Rozumovsky? What's he working on at the moment?

"He's working," replied Nemyrych, "on a new work."

"How interesting! And has Petrenko returned from Canada, where he went with a delegation from the Ukraine Society?"[27]

"Listen, junior, you know so much that the idea involuntarily comes to mind,..." began Hryts, narrowing his eyes.

"That it's time to bump me off, eh?" Bilynkevych laughed happily and asked a new question: "Have you seen the journalist Vitalii Korotych lately?[28] How is he?"

"Fine," replied Nemyrych.

"And will the last book of Semen Kovtun's trilogy be published soon?"

"No," replied Nemyrych.

"Why not?"

"Paper shortage," replied Nemyrych.

"I can't wait for the third book of that trilogy."

"None of us can."

"And were you at the funeral of the poet Petro Harkavy?"

"No."

"And how was it?"

"Dignified."

"And is it true that Zadorozhnẏ himself made a speech there?"

Lord, what mugs, good thing that Khoma's here at least, or they'd go for me, the gropers, unshaven, reeking of smoke, like illustrations from Lombroso,[29] all of them, shoving, swearing, shouting, it's not a bar, it's hell, it's the end of the world, where the hell is the can, where have they hidden it, what a fool I am, I shouldn't drink that much beer, Khoma is saying something, he's so attentive and charming today, there, this is what you call a festival, sitting in this stinking snake-pit, the whole world will pass us by while we sit around, honestly, it wasn't worth coming, well, here we are at last, oh no, I knew it, what do you expect, what an abomination, I haven't seen anything this bad for ages, Lord, look at this stuff scratched on the walls, I hope Khoma waits there right in front of the door, but he wouldn't go anywhere, surely, this door doesn't even lock from inside, hope I don't brush up against anything, thank God, at least the zipper hasn't jammed, I guess Martofliak is already plastered, he can't even drink beer, so much booze in his blood, wants to be a big brave Cossack: "go by yourself," that's for his mates' benefit, but when we're by ourselves it's always, "I can't live without you, Sunshine," ah, that's better, I was ready to burst, how about that, some vermin has even scratched the trident[30] into the wall, call that reviving national symbols and resurrecting the Spirit, oh no, damn, it had to get jammed, all I needed was to be stuck in this hole mucking around with a zipper, there, at last, no warm water, of course, but lo and

behold, here's a piece of soap—what class! only in Chortopil, may the demons rip it apart, my face has gone red something awful, better not drink any more, where's my beau, here I am, Khoma darling, "all done," what chivalry on your part—"anyone would have done it in my place," there's those gorillas again, don't let go, Khoma, I'll call the others, we made it, let's go on, where the hell's that table, can't see a thing, there's Martofliak, he's dived head first into a tankard, drunkard, deadbeat, father of my children …

"Is it true that Zadorozhny himself made a speech there?" asked Bilynkevych.

"Are you still pestering us with your questions, my angel?" Khoma, who had just returned to his seat, ruffled Bilynkevych's blond locks. "Stop that, or I'll tell Matsapura to throw you out of the ORGANIZING COMMITTEE."

"Why?" Bilynkevych blinked.

"Not why, but what for."

"What for?"

"For being drunk and disorderly!"

Bilynkevych laughed with relief. He had probably believed they could throw him out.

"Listen, didn't you say something about a restaurant in the neighbourhood?" Martofliak asked firmly.

"Yes, there's the Marketplace Restaurant next door."

"And we could get dinner there?"

"Yes, but it would be a good idea to check into the hotel. I'm responsible for you."

"Stop nagging! We've got to have dinner. Then we'll go to the hotel."

The company ardently supported Martofliak as the true leader of his generation. Only Marta shifted uneasily in her chair, but she understood that there was no way out.

"Well, let's go, then," agreed Bilynkevych, and, inserting a tenner into the pocket of a passing waiter, headed in a direction opposite to the one they had expected.

"Where are we going?" asked Martofliak dubiously.

"There's a service passage here. Straight from the bar to the restaurant via the cellars. Bodio, open the black door!" he shouted to the barman.

"The Black Door," repeated Martofliak. "Nice name for a book of poetry, eh?"

The massive black door was duly opened, and the friends disappeared down an underground passage dimly lit by the occasional electric bulb.

It seems that under each city lies another city with its own streets and squares, its own customs and secrets, I suppose I've always suspected as much but haven't checked up for myself, I didn't try, why check up on what you're certain about anyway, so now we're walking through the Middle Ages, a floor below is the pre-Christian era, then the mammoths, then, I guess, the Mesozoic and so on, there's no end to this downward progression, it's like my novel in verse, I'm always going deeper, but the bottom is unreachable, so I'll never finish it, but to hell with that, the main thing is that we're here at the festival and I'm ecstatic about seeing you marvellous fellows, my brothers—you, Khomsky, who can extract poetry even from shit, and you, Hryts, born in Karaganda,[31] forever wearing that black streak of hair across your forehead like a mark of mourning, and you, Yurko Nemyrych, who is dying every day in this insane world while everyone thinks that you're just posturing, you guys are good, you're great, and I'd give up all the gold of this earth for a single line of poetry by any one of you, for the happiness of blundering blindly with you through these dank Middle Ages from one pub to another in the company of this courteous youth, I've forgotten his name, but he's well-behaved, the whelp, and thus we move on so we may emerge in light, we walk towards the music as though drawn by the scent of vodka, and we'll drink a toast to our existence, lads, glory be that you exist, cheers!

There proved to be a black door at the other end as well, and in due course the whole company found itself in the very heart, in the restaurant's holy of holies, the prodigious kitchen with its delirious hissing and bubbling, red-hot frying pans and sizzling fish, frenzied screeches of the poultry saw, with plantations of salads, oils, sides of pink and brown meat, and a great army of schnitzels lined up for execution, raw, half-raw, and almost done; it seemed that the whole of our limitless country had selflessly laboured all year so that today all of this could come together here, in Chortopil's Marketplace Restaurant, along with mounds of leftovers and buckets of dishwater, dirty plates and spat-in cups, countless waiters, cooks, and various other types, legions of whom always mill around here at this time of the evening, and Bilynkevych leads the way as though into his own house, and everyone feels safe and reassured, for look—a few words murmured to the orangutang in the black suit and we're being taken to a table, this is unbelievable, a Table for Six that's free at such a time, but it's a fact, Bilynkevych knows his stuff, he's even managed to check your things in the cloakroom, and all of you, so relieved and at ease, sit down at the table in order, as Martofliak has put it, to have dinner.

For dinner you've ordered vodka and an unusual brandy called "White Stork," a dry Hungarian wine for Marta, and all sorts of similar stuff. Another Bodio (all waiters in Chortopil seem to answer to this name), wearing on his face the expression of a demure sphinx, has jotted down the immensely long list of dishes that you crave. Now you can calmly check out the customers and (Yurko, don't be a scrooge) smoke Gauloises.

Most of the public was in a state of increasing euphoria. It was, on the whole, a perfect menagerie. At such moments the seeds of friendship and love are sown, as one could easily read from the flushed complexions of the assembled. Animated dialogues and nervous kisses, people running out and coming back, sitting in the wrong places, and finishing off other people's schnitzels—all this, as well as the extinguishing of cigarette butts in salads, made it possible to conclude that the festival, whose beginning was little more than two hours away, would be successful and relaxed. The women had already reached a stage of behaviour where it is practically impossible to distinguish professional prostitutes from decent housewives, and the men had merged into a collective and many-faced portrait of an audacious businessman or some other phenomenal son of a bitch.

"Friends," said Martofliak, a touch of emotion in his voice, "before they bring the roast rabbit, I invite each of you to recite your most recent poem. You've all scribbled something down recently, I trust?"

"I've written a genuine May poem, which, I believe, suits the occasion," announced Khomsky. "But first let us drink, for my mouth is terribly dry."

Having done as he suggested, the company settled down to listen. And they heard the following:

> Tenderest blossoms of trees in the wood,
> Sublimest exertion of beauty and good,
> How gladly in your verdant land I'd remain
> Where warm bark is scented by juices of rain ...

"Not bad," Martofliak interrupted him, "but that's not yours, it's Andrukhovych's."[32]

"By the way, has he turned up?" Nemyrych asked.

"I don't think so," said Martofliak. "I've heard that he's writing some prose just now."

"Fascinating!" said Bilynkevych, reminding them of his existence.

"And who is this pleasant-looking youth sitting here in our midst?" said Shtundera, casting him a sidelong glance.

"Have you forgotten, or what?" Bilynkevych, taken aback, responded jovially.

"Friend, please remember one fundamental thing," said Khomsky. "The people present here have not seen each other for nearly three months. Right now they would like to catch up with each other. For this reason you ought not to interrupt their conversations, but to behave as though you were not here at all."

"Sorry," mumbled Bilynkevych.

"Well then. Now, since I've done my bit and we're reciting in turn, you're next, Martofliak. But, if you please, only after we've had another drink," commanded Khomsky.

Nothing came of Marta's protest against such a ferocious tempo. Then Bodio materialized with a large platter of various nutritious dishes. More glasses were filled. Nemyrych was itching to propose a toast, so the poems were temporarily forgotten.

"Beloved friends," he began with an air of complete sincerity, "I must confess that in this world relatively few things are worth anything at all. I suppose that, being very much alone, we all know this. It requires no comment, as they say. In any case, I'm sure all of you understand that perfectly. There can scarcely be anyone who doesn't, or pretends not to. Even if there were someone like that here, I wouldn't believe that he really doesn't understand. These are, as they say, commonplace truths, which is why we understand it so well. Speaking for myself, I'm almost certain that we're of one mind about this—otherwise I'd begin to doubt that there's anything at all in this world that we can understand. Then we'd have no choice but to admit that in this world we understand nothing. And that, as they say, would be very sad. So we have every reason to believe that we understand, or at least want to understand, something. And what we want to understand in the end is not such a great deal. But for us it's very important, because without it we're not ourselves, but simply irrational creatures that neither understand nor wish to understand anything. I think I've already said that few things in this world are worth anything. Let's drink to that!"

"Was he imitating Gorbachev?" Bilynkevych inquired of Martofliak once the toast had been consummated.

"Now, I ask you, who is this talkative youth sitting here in our midst?" asked Hryts, somewhat more sharply than before.

"I thought we had come to an arrangement, buddy," Khomsky reminded Bilynkevych.

"I'm sorry once again, but all of you are so interesting I can't help it …

"Did anyone invite him to join us?" asked Hryts, pursuing his inquiry.

"No, Hryts, he is carrying out his official duties," Khomsky assured him.

Bilynkevych shrank, seriously unnerved this time. Fortunately, however, a pause descended upon the conversation, coinciding with the devouring of hams and sausages, as well as tomatoes, cucumbers, and mushrooms.

"If you like, I'll tell you the plot of my novel," said Khomsky after a while, wiping his lips with a napkin.

"What is it called?" asked Martofliak.

"*The Miscreants*. It's a novel in short stories."

"Go ahead, but tell it so we understand," demanded Nemyrych.

"Okay. The action takes place at the beginning of the century in a little provincial town in Galicia. I'm going to describe in some detail the first aeroplane flight of a certain count. He rises up into the sky and performs three full loops above a field where crowds of astonished spectators have gathered. The principal of a private Gymnasium wants to seduce one of his female pupils and turns to a hypnotist for help. Then Archduke Ferdinand[33] arrives in the town attended by a whole regiment of cuirassiers who, it turns out, have long been planning to assassinate him. They are part of a terrorist organization headed by the old hypnotist. The trial of the Gymnasium principal begins, but he manages to save his bacon because the court proceedings are interrupted by an earthquake. The schoolgirl, who is praying in a church at the time, is swallowed up into the earth together with the church. She ends up in a hitherto unknown underground country. In the meantime the pilot, whom I introduced at the very beginning, can't land his plane because everything has been destroyed by the earthquake."

"Wonderful!" exclaimed Martofliak, ascertaining first that Khomsky had finished.

"I understood practically nothing," confessed Marta.

"I don't understand all of it either," agreed Khomsky, "but for some reason I like it very much."

It was after toasting Khomsky's superb tale that the companions became aware of a massive miscreant with a shaven head who had cruised past their table a number of times, his facial expression closely resembling that of a shark. He cast a number of exploratory glances in your direction, though it was difficult to determine whether this was good or bad. In the corner of the room you noticed a secluded table at which this oaf was seated with several other thugs who looked rather like him, if somewhat younger. It was strange that in the atmosphere of semi-insanity that pervaded the restaurant, Sharkface and his partners maintained an absolutely cool and businesslike air.

Bodio, however, dispersed your momentary unease by bringing out six hot Hutsul schnitzels and, in response to popular demand, another three hundred grams of vodka.

"Rostyk, don't drink any more," said Marta softly.

"I won't," promised Martofliak. "Not more than necessary. In the meantime I propose a toast to the fact that all of you exist!"

The vodka was still trickling down their gullets when Hryts nudged Martofliak under the table with his foot and said, "I've got something to tell you. Do you mind if we go out for a minute?"

They left, and four of you remained at the table.

"You can see he shouldn't drink any more today," said Marta.

"Marta, my dear, I assure you that everything will be fine," said Nemyrych with conviction. "Rostyk is a man of extraordinary endurance."

"I know better than you about his endurance or lack of it," insisted Marta.

"You look like a movie star tonight," Khoma whispered in her ear.

"If Martofliak can't help drinking, then he has to drink, otherwise there's something I don't understand," asserted Nemyrych.

"Do you know who just walked past our table?" asked Bilynkevych, suddenly reminding the others of his presence.

You looked at him inquiringly.

"That's Petia."

"And who the hell is he, that you pronounce his name with such reverence?" asked Nemyrych.

"He's king of the racketeers."

"Maybe we should get out of here," said Marta, uneasy again.

"Show him our heels? That's out of the question!" said Nemyrych, getting worked up. "We've got to give a dignified account of ourselves."

In the foyer Hryts and Martofliak were smoking.

"Rostyk, do you realize what shit we're in?" Hryts was saying. "It's totally screwed me up. They're everywhere. Listen, old buddy, this guy could be as high as the rank of KGB captain. Where did he come from, who brought him?"

"He was waiting for Khomsky at the station. He said Matsapura sent him."

"All the worse for Matsapura. Listen, Rostyk, old buddy, I can smell them. This is shit, and it's really scary."

"I don't think you're right. What would be the point for them? He really is exactly what he says—a boy from the Komsomol, and nothing more."

"Don't be so gullible. How can a simple boy from the Komsomol be familiar with all these tricks?"

"What tricks?"

"Why, the underground passage, the keys, all the waiters bowing to him, he finds a table for us right away. And you saw how he wormed his questions into the conversation?"

"Well, he's just interested."

"He's interested, I'll grant you that. Listen, Rostyk, when are you going to America?"

"Next month some time. I haven't got my ticket yet."

"You know what? Take these ten dollars, but don't let anyone see."

"What do I want them for, Hryts?"

"I'm giving them to you. Buy something for Marta. She's fantastic, old man."

"Thanks."

"You understand, there's so much shit around. We have to stick together. I hate them all, do you understand? Come on, I'll throw the truth at him, and then we'll bash his face in—how about it?"

"No, there's no need for that."

"Why are you being so careful, so well-behaved? You've got to hit him between the eyes, believe me! If you don't want to, I'll do it myself."

"Hryts, we'll just complicate the situation. We just need to get rid of him gently somehow."

"Listen, why are you being such a wimp? What are you, some kind of aristocrat?"

"You'd be better off telling me how things are with Yurko."

"Really bad, Rostyk."

"How do you know?"

"His doctor told me. The last tests have confirmed it."

"Oh, Lord!"

"Anything can happen. He knows everything, by the way."

"So, in that case ..."

"It's really bad, Rostyk, understand? And to cap it all off there's this slimeball here worming his way into our souls."

"Do we have enough to pay the bill?"

"It won't come to more than a hundred and fifty. If you want, I'll get him out here right away and let him have it. I can, you know—easily."

"Yes, Hryts, you can, but, believe me, it's not what you think. Please. Take it easy. Have you finished your smoke?"

"Yes. Shall we go in?"

"Yes. We'll have another drink. Listen, maybe he's just a queer?" speculated Martofliak.

"Either that or the other."

"Or both."

They returned to the table just as Khomsky was pouring drinks.

"We thought you weren't coming back," said Nemyrych.

"But there's still some booze left," Martofliak contradicted him.

"Rostyk, I'm asking you—please," begged Marta.

"Mr. Martofliak, when exactly are you departing for America?" asked Bilynkevych with a hiccup.

Hryts, though he said nothing, gave Rostyslav an unambiguous look.

"What does it matter," said Rostyk. "America is another world."

"Are you going to contact some editorial boards or publishers over there?"

"Excuse me, what's your name?" Martofliak asked genially.

"Ihor."

"For some reason I thought it was Ivan. You answered to Ivan before!"

"I didn't want to contradict you."

"I see! You know, Ihor, I'm sorry, but we don't like your questions very much."

"I was doing my best," said Bilynkevych, crestfallen.

"Don't be offended," said Martofliak, slapping him on the back.

"Look, the band's coming out." Nemyrych pulled a face. "Now they'll start up their hayseed music and we won't be able to talk."

"Do we want to order anything else?" asked Khomsky.

"Of course," confirmed Martofliak. "Brandy and something to eat."

"I can recommend the potato pancakes," said Bodio, who was just changing the settings, from behind Marta's shoulder.

"Ah, potato pancakes—what divine fare!" enthused Nemyrych. "Six servings with mushroom sauce, please!"

Bodio nodded knowingly and vanished like a magician.

Meanwhile Bilynkevych, who had anxiously been trying to think of ways to rehabilitate himself in front of everyone, finally had an idea.

"Would you mind if I invited Petia to our table?"

"That would be interesting," said Nemyrych.

"Providing he doesn't stay long," demanded Khomsky.

"I don't want him here," objected Marta.

"Call him!" decided Martofliak on hearing Marta's opinion. Once Bilynkevych had joyfully left them, he asked, "Who's Petia?"

"Petia is king of the racketeers," explained Nemyrych. "There he is over there—looks like a shark."

"I'm going," said Marta.

"Go," Martofliak agreed.

"I promise you, everything will be fine," said Khomsky, placing the palm of his hand on Marta's.

"They've gone completely nuts," said Marta, refusing to be comforted.

Petia didn't keep you waiting too long and approached your table, accompanied by the unsteady Bilynkevych.

"Allow me to introduce some poets, good friends of mine," Bilynkevych said in Russian. "They're very good poets, very famous."

"Petia," said the miscreant with a friendly smile.

He kissed Marta's hand, then shook hands with everyone in turn. Khomsky poured him a drink.

"To our acquaintance." The shark raised his glass and poured it into his gaping maw.

It was now possible to examine him more closely. He had a rather round, fat-cheeked face with a little scar on his forehead and was slightly goggle-eyed. His neck, which was short but thick as a bull's, was well tanned and adorned with a heavy gold chain. The rest of him consisted of a body wrapped in stone-washed denim. Also remarkable was his right hand, thickly encrusted with rings, each of which, evidently, had some mystical function.

Everyone followed the toast with a bite to eat, after which there was a polite silence.

"You've come for a vacation?" Petia asked finally, in Russian.

"Yes, for the festival of the Resurrecting Spirit," explained Bilynkevych on everyone's behalf.

"That's good, you did the right thing," purred the king. One might have called his voice a double bass. "But why are you answering for them, can't they speak?"

"They only speak in verse," giggled Bilynkevych. "Dear colleagues, for acquaintance's sake and to honour our guest Petia, I propose that each of you now recite a poem."

Hryts ground his teeth, and all the others gave Bilynkevych such a glare that he immediately grasped the extent of his tactlessness. But it was too late.

"I'd be delighted to hear them," said Petia encouragingly.

But nobody spoke.

"I like Esenin[34] very much, by the way," said Petia, trying to ease the embarrassing situation. "Do any of you remember Esenin?"

"You should understand," said Khomsky, taking a deep breath, "that we do like him."

"Wonderful. Then recite something of his."

"But at any given moment we prefer doing what we want to do," continued Khomsky, "not what you tell us to do."

"Colleagues, I have a toast I want to make." Nemyrych rose, a full glass in his hand. "Fill your glasses, for I'm about to speak."

Petia, who had blinked at Khomsky's answer, now readied himself to listen.

"Dear friends!" Nemyrych began, "human beings are made in such a way that they never have enough of anything. They shackle themselves by their own efforts to the chains, even gold ones, of material existence. And with these chains around their necks they live their brief temporal span. They rob their neighbours and, when necessary, even fire pistols at them. This is sad but true. The main thing is that human beings never stop to think about the purpose of all this. For whatever happens, in the end someone will always be quicker on the draw than you are. And the end is well known—it's the same for all of us jointly and for each of us individually. But all human beings are stubborn and deliberately blind, thinking that for them an exception will be made in the heavens, and that all will be forgiven them, and that they will be granted the eternal bliss of wearing denim and indulging nightly at restaurants, as all of us have done today. But sometimes they also hear an inner voice that prophesies, 'So what, you're not immortal, and even if you get a sumptuous funeral, and flowers straight from Brazil for your grave in midwinter, and a granite headstone with your profile in bronze, and even if your buddies come from all over the U-double-S-R to pay their last respects, even if their speeches alternate with Esenin's verses, even if all this!—you still won't be here tomorrow on this earth!' And although human beings seldom shudder, they shudder upon hearing that inner voice, yet, like sharks, they continue doing the same old thing and refuse to repent. Let us drink to human beings, stubborn and foolish, shackled to the gold chains of existence!"

"That was your swan song, dude," said Khomsky, when they finished drinking.

Petia didn't know whether to be angry or to thank Nemyrych for the beautiful toast. But he seemed to have grown somewhat sullen.

At that point the music finally started playing, giving rise to a new and exciting subplot.

"I'd like to dance with you," said the king to Marta.

Marta was about to fire off her favourite "what will you think of next," but took fright and said nothing.

"I'd like to dance with this chick," Petia repeated in a much louder voice, looking her in the face.

There you are, Martofliak, you've got a problem, now you should say or do something, or maybe let her dance, nothing can happen to her, the shark won't eat her, the mother of your children, God's will be done, why are you sitting as if you've shat yourself, and she's giving you that imploring look that says say or do something, how can I stand this pleading look of hers, well work something out, you great poet, why are you sitting here with your tongue up your arse contemplating your empty glass, you beard with two ears, do something, the whole world is watching ...

But Khoma gets up, all politeness, and says, "Sorry to disappoint you, but the first dance was promised to me. Come, Marta, my dear!" And he gestures in invitation.

Marta gets up (what else can she do?) and meekly follows Khomsky into the semidarkness where couples are doing a slow dance. Bilynkevych, though he's still there, appears to be cowering. Petia surveys them all with an unhurried look, as though memorizing their faces.

At this terrifying moment Nemyrych pulled his book from his pocket, wrote a few words on the title page, and presented it to the king.

"Thanks." Petia put the book into the breast pocket of his denim jacket without even reading the title. "Well, I'll be off. The boys are waiting. Have a good time."

All of you got up to give him a dignified farewell.

"I thought you were a jollier crew," said Petia before departing.

"Ihor," said Martofliak, "what do you think, who is more of a dead man—Khoma or Nemyrych?"

"I am, I think," said Nemyrych on Bilynkevych's behalf.

But that was already another topic.

The restaurant's dining room is ancient, its wooden wall panels are carved with views of Chortopil (the town hall, apothecary's shop, post office, bank, concert hall), big chandeliers fashioned from wood and brass by Hutsul master craftsmen hang from the ceiling, but here, above the dancers, they are dimmed, intimacy reigns here, as does seduction.

Marta, I can feel all of you, you are supple and warm, your movements are as I want them, we complement each other, it's only a dance, yet you're so close, I'm not Martofliak, don't do that, little girl, I only wanted to help you, you and Martofliak, I saved the day, I'm super, my timing is always perfect, I couldn't leave you to the mercy of that monster, I can imagine what he would have done to you, you're so warm and supple, everything's whirling inside my head—you, the music, the vodka, the danger, to hell with it, life's worth living, I'd carry you in my arms, duchess, lady, dancing queen, flying woman, don't torment me just now, because I'm crazed, I could abduct you, I'm a giant, I'm a spring, I'm an uncontrollable volcano at the festival of the Resurrecting Prick!

"Orest dear, I'm so grateful," whispered Marta.

"It was nothing. I've always dreamt of pulling off something like that," answered Khoma. "Would you have danced with that creep?"

"Another second and I would have. I was scared that in another minute he would do something awful, and I couldn't let that happen."

"Were you afraid of him?"

"Yes, very. He's really scary."

"I think he's a nice guy."

"The things you say! I was also afraid for Martofliak. If I'd gone dancing with that fiend, he might have …"

"What?"

"Done something."

"He would have been really spaced, Marta. Like all true masochists."

"He's just a big baby."

"True. A golden boy. You have a wonderful husband, Marta."

"Are you making fun of me?"

"Not at all. I'm absolutely serious."

"I like the way you dance."

"Thank you. You have beautiful breasts."

"Khoma, you're not really like this. You always want to play the cynic or the mocker. But you're not really what you pretend to be."

"None of us is really what we pretend to be. Hryts is really very trusting and compassionate. Nemyrych is introspective and indecisive. Your Martofliak is fearless and bold."

"Are you being prickly again?"

"Yes. Thanks for the dance, madame."

Marta and Khomsky returned to the table as their friends attacked the crackling potato pancakes that Bodio had just delivered. As for the three hundred grams of vodka, they had finished them off and Bodio had been dispatched for the next two hundred and fifty.

"Bugger-all is what any of you understands about Antonych's poetry!" yelled Martofliak, trying to shout over the din of the dance that had just begun.

"There's only one key to his poetry," Nemyrych responded, "and each of us has it between his legs!"

"What a charming welcome," said Marta, sitting down.

"Oh, had your fill of dancing, have you?" Martofliak observed, then proceeded with the discussion. "That key fits anyone! But it's not enough to get at Antonych! You can apply as much as you like of your fucking jerked-off Freudianism, but you'll never get to the heart of Antonych even if you shit yourself trying!"

"And how do you know that you alone have got to the heart of Antonych, how do you know that I haven't, motherfucker?"

"Because you talk absolute bullshit, absolutely meaningless trash about *The Book of Leo*."[35]

"Who, me? I never said a word about *The Book of Leo*! I was a bit disparaging about the poem you recited here and I didn't like."

"Shit, I couldn't care less if you don't like it for a hundred years, I need your opinion like ashes up my arse!" said Martofliak, capping off the discussion, not least because two hundred and fifty new grams of vodka had appeared on the table.

"Rostyk, which particular cities are you going to visit in America?" asked Bilynkevych indistinctly, his tongue in something of a tangle.

"I'm delighted that we're already on first-name terms," remarked Martofliak in lieu of a reply.

"Who is he, this lousy dickhead with the rosy cheeks?" said Hryts, who had been silent for some forty minutes.

"I'm your friend, Hryts," explained Bilynkevych.

"But I don't think you're our friend. You're the KGB major's friend."

"No, honestly, it's time to get out of here," said Marta, getting upset again.

"Who are you?" continued Hryts. "I know everyone here. I know Orest Khomsky, he's a wonderful poet from Lenig ... from Leningrad, I know Rostyk Martofliak, he's a grand poet, he's my friend, I know his beautiful wife Natalia ..."

"Marta," Bilynkevych corrected him.

"Marta," repeated Hryts. "I know Yurko Nemyrych, he's a colossal poet and a wonderful friend, I know myself. But who are you? Can anyone tell me anything about this strange man?"

Everyone was silent. Then Bilynkevych began to explain.

"I'm a member of the ORGANIZING COMMITTEE, you see ..."

"You're an insolent pig," interrupted Hryts, smiling.

"Hryts, don't, I asked you not to," said Martofliak.

"Sorry, he went a bit overboard," said Nemyrych to Bilynkevych.

"Yurko, tell him, he'll listen to you," Bilynkevych began to whimper, "I've tried so hard for all of you ..." And a tear rolled down his cheek.

"Hryts, that's enough!" said Martofliak firmly. "He's not a bad guy, even if he's with the KGB."

This phrase unexpectedly calmed Shtundera. In the meantime Khoma, who made the impression of being the soberest of everyone present, inquired discreetly of Bilynkevych, "You wouldn't be able to lend me two hundred until tomorrow?"

"I would. Why?"

"Then settle the bill with Bodio, and I'll pay you back tomorrow."

"What are you talking about, my dear Orest, there's no need to pay back anything," said Bilynkevych, waving his arms.

"I don't drink at anyone else's expense," replied Khomsky sharply. "What time is it, colleagues?" he asked the others in a loud voice.

"It's starting in half an hour," replied Marta.

"Right. Listen here, Bilynkevych." Khomsky was speaking as crisply as the commander of a submarine. "Go to Bodio and pay him, but add on a coffee and fifty grams of brandy for each of us. Then come back and tell me the total. Off you go!"

Bilynkevych flew off as if he had wings. He was overjoyed that they were treating him like a human being again.

"I ask now for your attention," said Hryts as solemnly as he could. "In a moment I'll recite my last poem. It's my best. It's about a man. It's rather long. I would ask you to listen and not to interrupt. It's a very new poem. I've said everything in it, as you'll hear. It's my second-last poem."

"The second-last or last?" asked Khoma.

"The last one doesn't count. This is the second-last. I asked you not to interrupt."

Everyone was listening. Martofliak was about to light the filter end of his cigarette, but Marta stopped him in time.

"I'll remember it in a moment. Just a moment. There's a colossal first line."

"Is that all?" asked Khoma.

"Don't interrupt. I'll remember it in a moment. It's in free verse."

Everyone was listening, but by now with somewhat bored expressions.

"I wrote it the day before yesterday. The one I wrote yesterday doesn't count."

"You wrote it the day before yesterday?" asked Khoma. "Then you should recite it to us in nine years' time. Seneca advised locking up anything you write in the drawer for nine years.

"You're both shits, you and your Seneca. Where's my manuscript?" Hryts was suddenly worried. "Ah, yes, I sold it for ten dollars, of course. But I'll remember it in a moment. It's quite fresh in my mind. It's a poem about a village."

"Or about a man?" Khoma needled him again.

"You don't understand a thing. You didn't know that man. I knew him. This poem is dedicated to his memory. One moment. I'm reciting."

And, closing his eyes, he began:

Grass, this green girl on an auburn slope,
each year it is new, snakes slither through it,
it houses the tiny windows of God's underground home,
and God looks from below through damp blades only ...

No, that's not it. I'll have it in a moment. Ah, yes:

... who looks from below through green blades only ...

No, "through damp blades only ..."

Just then Bodio showed up once more with the coffees and the final brandies. Bilynkevych whispered in Khomsky's ear, "One hundred and eighty-three rubles and forty-five kopeks."

"Write it on your forehead so I don't forget," advised Khoma.

"Enough! I can't remember!" confessed Hryts. "I won't recite any more. You wouldn't understand anything anyway, my boy." And he patted Bilynkevych on the cheek.

The coffee smelt fine. The brandy, too. You began to hurry, because you sensed that outside the square was beginning to seethe. Most of the customers were leaving the restaurant.

Bilynkevych suddenly leapt to his feet, brandy in hand, and crowed:

"Gentlemen, please drink to our father, Stepan!"[36]

"I told you so," remarked Hryts, but he drank up. As did all the others.

"Rostyk, bring me some books from America, okay?" Bilynkevych began pestering him in the cloakroom as they were getting their things.

"All right, old man, I'll bring you something interesting," promised Martofliak. "Say, the *Guinness Book of Records*."

"No! I don't mean books like that. I'll tell you later, all right?"

He didn't leave them alone even when they finally made it out into the square, which was full to overflowing with people, noisy, and lit up with multicoloured floodlights, lanterns, and torches. Something unbelievable was about to take place.

And then, when the Chortopil town-hall clock struck twelve, it began. From the former Street of the Sisters of the Sacrament there emerged a grand procession of maskers, headed by several functionaries with organizing committee armbands and megaphones in their hands. Upon entering Market Square, the procession broke up into a number of streams, and here they are coming past us, beating drums and timpani, blowing trumpets and horns, playing harps and psalteries, stringed instruments and flutes, cymbals both sonorous and resonant, there is a whole sea of them—in masks and with painted faces, they are innumerable!

There were Angels of God, Gypsies, Moors, Cossacks, Bears, Studiosi, Devils, Witches, Naiads, Prophets, the Basilian Fathers in brown cassocks, Jews, Pygmies, Uhlans,[37] Whores, Legionnaires, Shepherds, Lambs, Cripples, Lunatics, Murderers, Bandits, Turks, Hindus, Sich Riflemen, Vagrants, Kobzars,[38] Heavy

Metallists, Samurai, Idlers, Serdiuks,[39] Oil-Pressers, Mamelukes,[40] Janissaries,[41] Saracens, Hebrews, Negroes, Patricians in togas, Sluts, Scribes, Liars with their tongues hanging out, Cretins, Zaporozhian Cossacks, Infantrymen, Musicians, Mohammedans, Malankas,[42] Malantsi,[43] Molls, Fallen Women, Hutsuls, Trojans, Sarmatians,[44] Hippies, the Blind, Trembita[45] Players, Harlots, Saints with cardboard haloes, Hetmans,[46] Monks, Punks, Tramps, Gossips, Troubadours, Butchers, Jurists, Bribe Takers, Drunkards, Physicians, Arabs, Brigands, the Dominican Fathers in white, Strumpets, Heroes, Beer Drinkers, Snout-Dippers,[47] Lard Eaters, Ragamuffins, Oakbreakers, Minstrels, Prostitutes—and it is impossible to enumerate all the others, for there were also Generals, Gorillas, Baboons, Paulicians,[48] Danaids,[49] Nanai,[50] Nymphs, Nivkh,[51] Assyrians, Albanians, Pickpockets, Lyre Players, Innkeepers, Macedonians, Brewers, Anachorites, Goat Skinners, Ukrainians, Midwives, Gnomes, Dryads, Bats, Black Cats, Frogs, Alchemists, Tarts, Lepers, Tatars, Abyssinians …

The din and clamour they created as they bit, kissed, grabbed by the hands, and swept into their stream all who did not object was beyond belief. Over their heads fluttered various absurd flags—green and violet, pink and white (striped), black and white (checked), red and blue, and others.

You move along at a short distance away from them, taking care not to lose sight of each other. Bilynkevych is hanging on to Martofliak, who would find the going difficult even without him.

In the meantime piles of all kinds of stuff are brought out of the tents, all of it shimmering and jangling, while on stages various tricksters pretend to eat fire or swallow knives, others are standing on their heads, some are reciting who knows what nonsense, others still are playing at cards or drinking vodka, and people are dancing in front of the monument to the first Komsomol members because someone has hung a sign on it that reads, "Dancing Here."

On one of the stages there's a pantomime where everything turns on juggling sausages, which might represent whatever you please. On another stage a joke competition is in progress, and a rather crude fellow hugging a microphone is telling the story of how a young man got married and what came of that.

"Repent!" a grey-haired prophet is shouting from another stage. "The moment of reckoning is drawing near! Do you know the number 666?"

"Yes!" they shout from the throng.

"Do you know that it is the number of the beast, and therefore the human number?"

"We do!"

"And what is three times 666?"

"We don't know!"

"I shall tell you. Three times 666 is 1998!"

"Really? So what?"

"The year 1998 will be the last. Prepare as you can, for you are all adulterers and evildoers and will be held responsible, in other words, you'll really get it in the arse — you'll be stuck for all eternity in boiling pitch, where you'll stink and suffer!"

He is applauded, not least because for a while he hovers above the stage, his arms outstretched like wings, and then his trousers fall down and on his bare behind everyone can read, in large letters, 19 98. There's nothing on his front. This is amazing, but it's quite possible that some optical illusion is at work. They are capable of anything, these charlatans.

A gentleman in an ancient hat and, what is more, whiskers so long that it would be convenient for him to tuck them behind his ears has laid out some paraphernalia straight on the pavement and is giving a loud commentary on his achievements:

"Honourable people! By me have been invented multitude interesting objects, also herbs and curative grasses! In early youth with me conversed spirit of young Lomonosov,[52] in result of which I *heute*[53] stand before you so virtuous and innocent. Who wants to acquaint closer, can. Who does not want, let him depart quick, for I am such who also foots-hands can break, no charge! No need to shove snout here, take up space. For normal people here I will *heute* be friend. Because I am like this: I am who I am, love my arse,

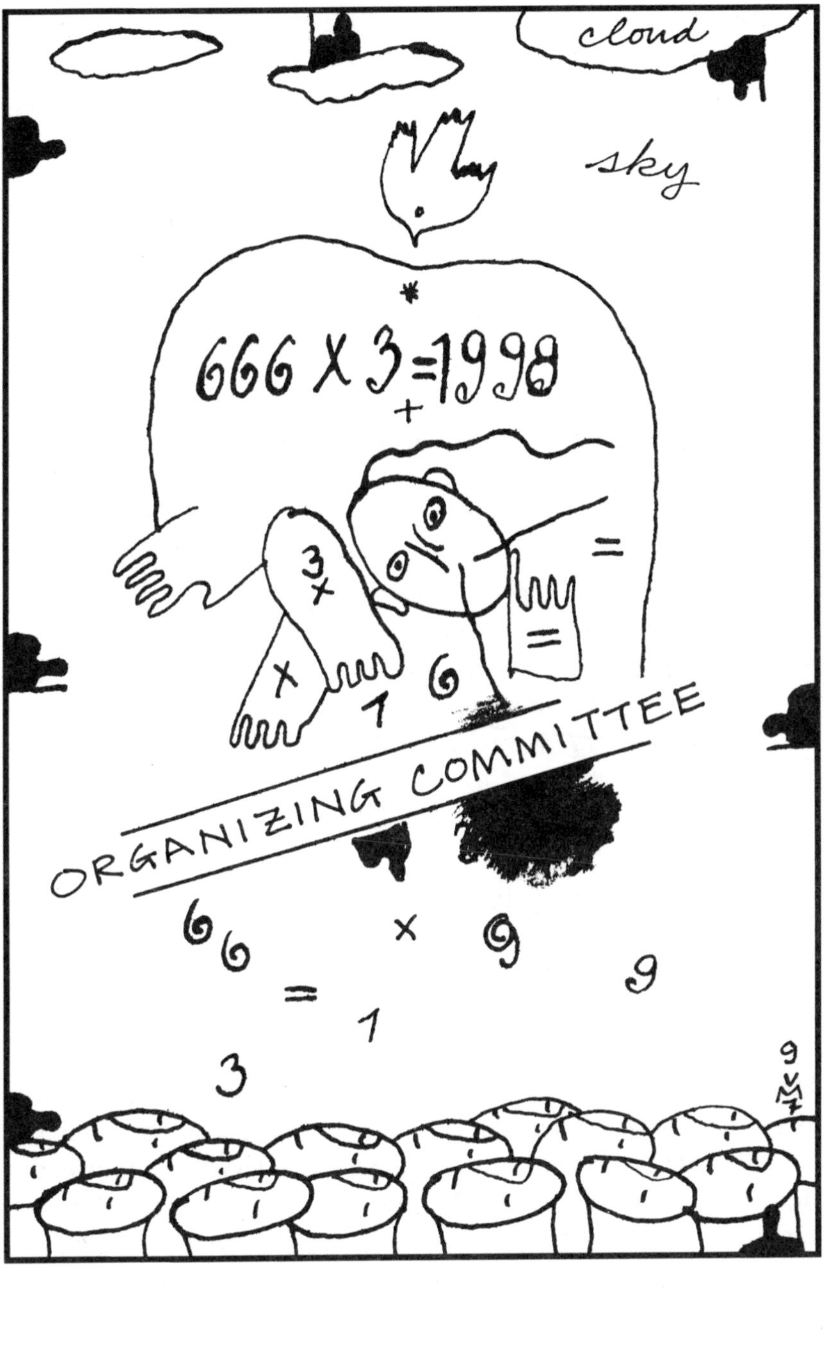

cloud
sky
666 X 3 = 1998
ORGANIZING COMMITTEE

gentlemen! Now in turn about each my author's projects, my fucking miraculous formulas. Powder to induce puking, diarrhoea, bleeding, pains and faintings, that is, swoons. Ingredients: black coffee, vodka Stolichnaya, sweat of horse, twisted spine of lizard-salamander, poke in mouth with cart-shaft, glass that is ground, poison of snake, vinegar also known as acetic acid—whichever preferred— plus human flesh in small quantity, tweezer-full at least! Ideal substance if people do not like you, bastards. Used by secret services of all Western powers, not used only here by stupid Ivan! If not interested, get out, *sehr schlecht*,[54] too bad, because by accident can smash skull or, *zum Beispiel*,[55] break spine!"

"That's Stasyk, an actor from Matsapura's theatre," Nemyrych explains, in case anyone were to mistake the salesman for a real maniac.

"I have the impression that everyone on this square is an actor from Matsapura's theatre," generalizes Martofliak, shaking himself free of the semiconscious Bilynkevych, who responds by gurgling something that sounds like "Glory to the Heroes."[56]

"What should we do with this sack?" asks Martofliak, pointing to the prostrate Komsomol member.

"Throw him into that barrel full of naked girls—let him sober up," suggests Hryts.

"Second of all, he might choke, and first of all, where do you see a barrel full of naked girls?"

"He has to check us into the Blue Mountain Hotel," Marta reminds everyone. "Without him they might not let us in."

"Well then, you drag him around!" exploded Martofliak. "I've had enough. I've done my Christian duty."

"I propose we put him beside that monument and let him sleep. Meanwhile we can wander around for another hour or two, then come back, wake him up, and go to the hotel," Nemyrych suggests.

"The idea is, on the whole, sound," says Hryts, "but instead of dragging him all the way to the monument, it would be simpler to stash him somewhere here, say, in the trunk of that car over there. Which, by the way, reminds me very strongly of something."

"That's Mr. Popel's Chrysler," says Nemyrych, coming to his assistance.

"Can anyone here open the trunk of a Chrysler?" asks Hryts, looking as if he were asking whether anyone knows how to open a tin can.

"Surely, old man, that trunk must be open," insists Nemyrych. "The car belongs to Mr. Popel, not some—pardon, Marta—cheap bastard! I'm pretty sure of that."

And all of you together pick up from the pavement the dead-weight of Bilynkevych, who at that moment is saying something like "heroes never die," and drag him over to the empty black Chrysler that has appeared out of nowhere in the middle of the crowd and the square, the trunk, of course, is unlocked, and with relief you throw Bilynkevych, paralysed by sleep, into it—let him rest, the son of a bitch, that's what he deserves.

Then you plunge once again into the festival—it belongs to you, you've been part of it for a good hour now, and yet something inside is resisting—it's not right, not right, though, on the other hand, it's just right, well done, Pavlo, you worked at it, got it together, and now a kobzar is singing about the red winding-cloth or about the red guelder rose, and students are staging a mystery-play about our Fatherland, and you can buy a horoscope at a free-enterprise stall or eat a kabob, or shoot arrows from a bow at a huge cardboard Stalin, or ogle the next-in-line backside of the next-in-line competitor in the "Supermiss" contest, or drink straight from a bottle, or make up your kisser with blue and yellow paint, or listen to the oratorio, or look at the sky through a telescope, or lose in the no-losers lottery, or have a fight with someone—just for the hell of it or over some little bitch—or juggle knives and oranges, or get pissed to the gills like Bilynkevych, or buy an amulet on a chain or a cross, or kick the bucket, or do some shooting at a moving target, or buy an old gramophone, or dance a ritual *arkan*[57] till morning, or sing in a small company about recruits and the red guelderrose or the red winding-cloth, or bathe with some girls in a barrel, or sleep in the trunk of a black car, or buy a copy of the Bible in Ukrainian, or the Koran in

Arabic, or a porn calendar, or a video cassette, or a Makarov pistol, or a set of stag's horns, or a rooster, or a hen, or a flag, or a pair of jeans, or a body, or God, or morphine, or spare ribs, or breasts, or beer, or water, or a pipe, or nails, or a hide, or a wound, or split and go to your hotel, or walk around here until morning, or die ...

These fires above, these soaring sparks, this devouring of flames, these baroque walls of buildings hung with garlands and green May branches, these statuettes carved into niches and gateways, strewn with confetti and streamers and smeared with excrement and sperm, these orange tents with a thousand attractions and a thousand rules, these towers above the gardens, these stone walls, this town hall with the highest spire in the world, these mountains above the town, these stars in the heavens.

This darkness in the town, these bats in the bell towers, these candles in the graveyard, these torture chambers in the cellars, these wells choked with bones, this junk in old rooms, these algae in the fountains, these garbage dumps on the slopes, these voices in underground passages, and also these rusting pipes and taps, peeling washbasins, filthy bathrooms, worn-out cutlery, torn sheets, broken china, buried bells, burnt books, armless crosses, these four horsemen.

These blue semicircles, these painted lips, sacred bruises, stigmata, dilated veins, bashed-in noses, crooked spines, these agile tongues, singing thighs, holey stockings, bared backs, bloodied fangs, sharp collarbones, gnawed breasts, these lanterns between legs, this radiance.

And you are powerless here to say anything, to change anything—you walk in circles like somnambulists, and each of you has his own planet and each will go his way, though you quite sincerely wanted only to stay together and do nothing stupid, but intoxication walks in your heads and the festival tramples you with its feet, you are minced like stuffing by a good cook, for, as Nemyrych said earlier, you are all alone, so it is doubtful whether your walking will lead to anything among these tents and stages, among these beautiful cripples, on this square surrounded on all sides by mountains and by Europe, where each of you will lose his way in his own manner, there, it's beginning, they're calling out, whistling, shouting, pulling at your sleeve, begging, demanding:

"Mr. Martofliak!"

And at last your waiting has borne fruit, Martofliak: the nation knows its poets, you are called, you are wanted, you begin signing autographs for these pleasant young people in embroidered shirts and stone-washed jeans, they are students, of course, they are crazy about your poems, among them Marta recognized the one who almost swooned from joy when he saw you on the bus.

You write all sorts of nonsense for them in their notebooks, on copies of your own books, on pictures of you, the most important thing is never to repeat any of your autographs, you must always be laconic, witty, profound, magnanimous, self-sufficient, highbrow. But this girl with eyes like plums and enthralling lips doesn't have a notebook, a copy of your book, or your photograph, Martofliak, and she asks you to write on her forehead, and you call for blue and yellow felt pens and inscribe her hot little forehead with your initials, bravo, encore, you kiss her hand, and now what? Your gang has stopped a few steps away and is angrily calling to you:

"Martofliak! Rostyk! Old buddy! Are you coming or not? What the fuck's going on?"

But right now you feel really comfortable, really at home, Martofliak. They're my friends, you explain obligingly to the students, poets too, by the way—Nemyrych, Khomsky, Shtundera— you haven't heard of them? Well, you'll hear of them yet, they're talented guys, some of their stuff works, who's that girl with them, I don't even know, everyone is laughing, you begin to take your leave, but the boy from the bus with the red-and-black badge mentions that not far away they have a table set, a guitar, unlimited booze, and couldn't you spend an hour with us—that would be great. Meanwhile the two plums look at you in a way that makes you shake off the remnants of your numbness and shout to your buddies.

"Yo! Do you hear? I'm leaving you for an hour!"

"Rostyk!" You hear Marta's voice and for a moment your eyes connect with her disconcerted look, but you blow them all a kiss meaning "piss off," and, surrounded by the noisy brood of students, you head for the place in the bushes where the guitar and set table are.

They take you by the arms, too bad they don't have a sedan chair or a litter, they would carry you on their shoulders, yes, and that morsel with your initials on her forehead as well, she has an unusual name—Zoreslava—actually it's not such a long way, you turn into a courtyard between some buildings not far from the square, and there on the new grass beneath cherry trees that are still blossoming a table has really been set, and at last they usher you toward it, a gas lamp gives off a warm glow, and all of you sit down noisily and drink a glass of something homemade, and then, of course, another.

You, Martofliak, love such moments dearly. They listen as if you were a prophet, every word worth its weight in gold, and you feel like the minister for external or internal affairs at a briefing: your replies are impressive and you are wonderful, Martofliak, it's been a long time since you've found yourself so attractive.

"Mr. Martofliak, can today's Supreme Soviet improve our situation?"

"Can a pig fly?" You answer this question with another.

"Then what should we be doing?"

"We must grow and we must act."

"Who will get the upper hand—the Catholics or the Orthodox?"

"As always, godlessness will get the upper hand. That's because for Ukrainians the number of embroidered cloths in their churches is more important than some Sermon on the Mount."

"Do you think martial law will be introduced?"

"I'm no prophet, but that's no solution."

"Will our national symbols be endorsed by parliament?"

"They have been endorsed by our history. They need no further endorsement."

"Do you believe in God? Will aliens help us? Will America help us? Will the International Monetary Fund save us? Will Hetman

Polubotok's[58] gold save us? Will the UN help us? Will Brussels help us? Will Geneva save us? Will love save us? Will Warsaw help us? Will Wałęsa like us? Will Israel save us? Will the Arabs believe us? Will the Tatars help us? Will the Turks support us?"

You, Martofliak, answer all of these queries easily and neatly, experiencing in the meantime a high from the increasing joyful clangour of the bell in your head, from the tiny palm of the little star Zoreslava in your hand, and from the profound reverent silence that accompanies your monologue:

"You know, friends, every step that we take is a step along a road. The ashes of empires can smother everything, but there is still the eternal wind, the movement of air, currents in the ozone. We can be saved only by the wind, only by the water in the rivers. Weapons at dawn are beautiful, they shine, they are lustrous. We all have these weapons with us—they are sharp, like the Word of God. Let us not forget the golden sun, the moss on the rock, the warm mirrors of autumn. Love girls—and they will give birth to your very selves. Raise bees and don't trample ants, and it will be returned to you a hundredfold. Grow grain, as it is written in the books, and tend flocks on the slopes. Carve wooden heroes, buy birds in cages, and set them free. Love the fish as you love all other symbols. Listen to your blood, for blood is the state. Respect each blade of grass, for grass is the nation, it is hope. Pray only when you see a shell or a bird or a wound. When at the end of summer you come to yourselves, understand that the road is endless. God is Love, God is Oil, and everything else as well."

Your words intoxicate you, as does this searing homemade hootch, Martofliak. They are ready to follow you. They are silent, they are writing something down in those confused heads of theirs, and they are pretending they have understood something of your ramblings, even though you understood nothing yourself, but you feel that this is what they need just now. The guitar appears, and a skinny, big-eared minstrel wearing glasses begins plucking the strings barely audibly, you have another drink, you feel good, Martofliak, the moist plums reflect a warm fire, all is quiet, angels are flying about, big-ears begins singing about some tragic campaign of the glorious Cossack Host from which no one has returned to this day, instead they wander through the wilderness not knowing where they are—in Europe, in Turkey, or, perhaps, in paradise. The song moves you to the point of tears, you crack your fingers, Martofliak, Zoreslava weeps, almost everyone else weeps, they smoke, drink some more, then weep again, for another song is beginning—one about bleached bones buried deep under St. Petersburg, and how nonetheless they sprout and their green shoots come up through the asphalt in spring, and St. Petersburg schoolgirls weave wreaths out of them, and they, your companions, gradually get up and start to dance here in the yard around the table, and someone takes the moist star Zoreslava away from you, she dances as well, and only two of you remain at the table, you and big-ears, who now sings a song about a mountain girl from the green forest and how she went picking berries and the Tatars caught her, but she ran away, and then she went to the river and the cursed Poles got her, but she ran away, and then she got married to a bearded man she didn't love and is suffering to this day.

You crumple your beard, Martofliak, and probably don't understand the song at all as it was intended, from time to time Zoreslava comes to mind, where can she be, they've all disappeared somewhere, they were dancing and then they disappeared, only you and big-ears are listening to each other, you recite poems to him, he sings to you, then you are simply silent for long stretches, and the night is like the sea, though the din from the square is still just audible here, on this patio in the middle of town, in this hospitable courtyard.

It seems you've had too much to drink, Martofliak, where the devil has she got to, I'd show her a real man, we would create a love tree, we would grow to the very skies, I would tear her like an ape tears apart paper, who's she with now, who's kissing her fingers?[59]

"Music is moving architecture,"[60] you continue your ratiocinations, even though big-ears seems to have nodded off. "Electrification is communism minus Soviet power.[61] In strength is the unity of the people.[62] This sweet freedom is the Word.[63] Your ideas bring me profound pleasure, Mr. Voltaire, but I would give my life to prevent you from expressing them freely."[64] After these reflections you get up and head for the garden, it's dark there and the grass catches at your feet, Martofliak, but at last you find what you sought: Zoreslava asleep on the grass, or, more precisely, on a coat spread on the ground, snuggled up to a sleeping brat, he has golden hair and a black-and-red badge, and she has your initials on her forehead, they are lying there, hugging each other like God's children, and in their dreams they can see their own heaven, what an idyll, could it be he didn't screw her, the jerk, the wimp, the premature baby, at least he should have helped to conceive a new Ukrainian.

But there's nothing to be done here now, you've got to go somewhere else. You return to the courtyard, passing big-ears who has fallen asleep at the table, his glasses have fallen off, he has thrown his head back and stuck out his Adam's apple, his snoring is unbearable, you get to the gate, Martofliak, and end up in the street—ancient walls all around you are overgrown with moss, ivy, and laurel, your unsteady footsteps resonate deeply. Where the hell is that Market Square or that hotel, I want to sleep, I want a woman, I want a smoke, I want a friend.

And I am alone in the whole world, and nobody needs me, so why did she look at me like that, I was snared by two plums, she's at least ten years younger but she gave me such a runaround, that Chortopil teaser, she got away at the last moment, and now I am alone in the whole world, which is naught but the vanity of vanities and makes absolutely no sense.

Passing a wide-open gateway you stop. There's someone there, Martofliak. Light-coloured hair, looks like a blonde with her back turned. How about that! Maybe I should pat her behind? But the blonde leans forward and vomits, and it turns out to be Bilynkevych, who has wandered into this street and is now retching in front of this gateway, and then he turns toward you and asks,

"Rostyk, will you bring me Dontsov[65] from America?"

"How did you get here?"

"Can you imagine, I was asleep in a car, in the trunk, that is, and then someone threw me out."

"Where are you heading? Take me to the hotel!"

"What do you want a hotel for? Let's go visit Marta instead."

"I don't want to visit Marta." You shudder, Martofliak.

"Not your Marta!" laughs Bilynkevych, wiping his snout with his sleeve. "The Marta who lives here, through this gate. She's a hooker. Let's pay her a visit—we can have a drink and a snack and then go to sleep."

"Is she young?" you ask, Martofliak.

"She's a sex-bomb," answers Bilynkevych as you ascend the steep wooden stairs. "She lives on the third floor. She has some booze. You'll like her."

"I have to go," Hryts pronounced suddenly. "I have to leave you."

"You too, Hryts?" asked Nemyrych.

"I wish you'd all …" Marta began angrily, but she looked as though she really wanted to cry. "Why the hell did I come here? I've got kids at home, and instead I follow that old half-wit."

"I've got to go," said Hryts, paying no attention. "It's bullshit, but I've got to."

"Business?" inquired Nemyrych.

"Yes, I've got to go."

"So piss off then, don't keep repeating 'I've got to go, I've got to go' like a zombie!" shouted Khomsky. "If you have to do something, you don't ask anybody's permission, you just do it. If you want to go, go. I'm not about to throw stones in your wake. Just don't stand around endlessly mouthing 'I've got to go', because I'm beginning to suspect that you don't have to go anywhere at all."

"No, I've got to go," said "zombie" Shtundera, pleasing everyone once more, and then he finally went.

He crossed the square, now in the spasms of acrobatic displays and tugs-of-war, but, before turning into the former Street of the Sisters of the Sacrament, he looked into a brightly coloured tent on which "Monster factory. Wishes granted" was written. This happened because he had conceived a wish to be different.

In the tent there were several guys and girls, most of them good-looking, who were offering all kinds of services imaginable.

"I'd like a haircut, please," said Hryts, taking a seat in front of a mirror.

"Would you like a Cossack *oseledets* cut?" asked a girl in a skirt so short that she seemed to be completely naked.

"Yes, an *oseledets*. Absolutely."

And she started cutting his hair, leaving only that well-known long, black tuft on his head. First she used scissors, then clippers, then shaved his skull with a razor, making it ever more shiny, while the black tuft—a real *oseledets* now—remained untouched.

"It really suits you," said the girl. "If I were you I'd never wear anything but an *oseledets*."

"Right," replied Hryts.

"You have a beautifully shaped head," she continued. "The *oseledets* and your mustache make you look unusual and sort of special."

"Yes, I know."

"You're the real Cossack type," she went on. "I guess you've got really pure genes. I hope you don't mind my being so personal."

"No, that's all right."

"You're so reserved. Maybe real Cossacks were like you—dark eyes, a long thin nose, a tanned lean face. You look like Bohun.[66] Or a young Mazepa.[67] Do you want me to highlight your eyes a bit? I've got mascara, lipstick and all sorts of make-up. Would you like that?"

"No."

"Maybe you'd like a massage? I do a fantastic massage. You'll feel really strong and invincible. Come on, get undressed behind that screen and I'll do you a massage. Everyone I've given a massage to has really liked it. You'll like it too."

"I've got to go," said Hryts, "I don't have much time."

"Whatever you like." The girl put her hand inside his shirt and

AT THE HAIRDRESSER'S

stroked his chest. "You look really nice in an *oseledets*. I want to have your child. You've got really pure genes."

"Thanks, I've got to go," said Hryts. He started for the exit, but saw a guy in a Sich Rifleman's uniform.

"Do you have a Cossack outfit?" Hryts asked him.

"I'm right out of Cossack gear. Sich Riflemen's gear too, for that matter," said the guy.

"But I really need one," Hryts insisted.

"You can have the one I'm wearing. Bring it back tomorrow morning. In the meantime I'll wear your clothes."

Hryts nodded gratefully and changed then and there. Boots, field jacket, trousers, two belts.

"Sorry, I don't have the service cap," said the guy. "But you've got a fine *oseledets*. You don't need the cap."

Minutes later they were transformed—Hryts was in the uniform of an officer of the Ukrainian Galician Army and the guy was in Hryts's denim rags.

"Come by tomorrow," said the guy as a farewell.

"Come by, I'll be waiting," said the girl with the naked legs, waving goodbye.

"Thanks. Got to go." Hryts spread his arms apologetically and walked out of the tent.

Now I have to find everything. I heard about it from the old man so many times that I've learnt all his words by heart. I've got to be there tonight.

The former Street of the Sisters of the Sacrament comes off Market Square, so it is just as noisy and bits of the festival flare up here as well. But farther away there are dark dead streets and squares, abandoned courtyards, boarded-up windows, twisted steps leading down into cellars. If, before reaching the end of Sacrament, you turn right, you'll easily find your way to the former Resurrection Square, where there's a wooden church. You can go around it from both sides, and, unless I've got something mixed up, it is from Resurrection Square that the road to Little Village begins, past the cemetery and the roadside chapel.

Before I was seventeen I didn't even know this was where my old man was born and grew up. I had guessed there was some secret in the past. I understood perfectly well that we had been deported: Ukrainians aren't born in Karaganda just like that. But I wasn't too interested in the details. It was after my old man's death that I got really into it.

"There's a cemetery there, Hryts, and a chapel next to it, understand?— and some people from Little Village are buried there, but only a few, because Little Village had a cemetery of its own. And a chapel and church as well. I've heard there's not a trace of anything left now—just as if nobody had ever lived there at all. There's a Little Village Nature Site near Chortopil, that's all. They burnt everything, you know."

They burnt everything, they burnt everything, they burnt everything, they killed everyone, they devoured everything, they smashed everything, they took everything, they messed up everything.

If I've passed the cemetery, the next landmark should be the sawmill at the corner of the former Quiet and Poniatowski streets. That's probably on the outskirts of Chortopil. This is where the track to Little Village begins. The track leads to a stone footbridge over the River, and then it's another ten minutes through the forest to the Little Village Nature Site.

We grew up as best we could, each of us. Later, when we moved to the Donbas,[68] everyone said we spoke in Polish. They didn't understand half of what we said. My old man didn't tell me he was born here. He wanted somehow to hide what he could never get back.

"So, Hryts, when you see the sawmill, you turn off and go uphill along the track. The younger of my uncles worked at that sawmill. He was only two years older than I was, so I didn't even call him Uncle. He was a technician. You don't know him, you couldn't, anyhow. He really loved clay. He made whistles, little horses, and deer from it. But remember—past the sawmill you go uphill. If you forget and go straight ahead, you'll miss Little Village and come out at Pretty Pond. They took a lot of people away from there as well, but not everyone as they did with us."

They didn't take everyone away, some of us remained, some of us remained, they didn't burn everything, they didn't take everything, they didn't tear everyone to pieces, they loved us, they helped us.

I won't forget, of course, I'll go uphill, the track is the same as it was forty or even a hundred years ago, there's the noise of the River already, it has the cleanest water in Europe, no industry on its banks, I'm climbing higher all the time, if you look back at Chortopil from here it looks as it does in the old engraving, those damned mutts, what are they barking at, though I suppose the whole place belongs to them this time of night, they've got the right, beautiful animals, let them bark.

"They used dogs to drive us out. They had about ten vicious dogs. All the way to the station the dogs ran along both sides of the road and barked at us in a frenzy. The horses were out of their minds with fright and galloped like mad."

My feet aren't used to these boots. I've only been walking an hour and I've already got blisters, they're probably bleeding. If they let the dogs loose on me now I won't be able to run away. I'll just have to kick them, I'll kick them with these boots, I'll kick them in the head and in the stomach.

"The roofs of their mouths were black. That kind of dog is really vicious. It's impossible to get on good terms with them. They only know how to tear you to shreds."

Below me the river is roaring like Niagara Falls. What if something has destroyed the footbridge in these forty years? How shall I get to Little Village? I'll have to ford the River. That's not so hard—the water's mostly very shallow, but swift as hell, it could probably knock you over. Those dogs are chasing me now—barking like mad, they've probably got black mouths. What fool lets such wild beasts out at night? They could rip your throat out, tear you to pieces. Chew off your dick and balls, that kind of thing. They liked mutilating the genitals. Otherwise it's very hard to make strong, proud men cry. The main point was to make them cry, I guess.

These dogs really are chasing after me. But they can't reach me, I'm already in the middle of the River, the stones underfoot are slippery, the water's cold, I can feel it through these boots and it's hard to keep your balance, but you offspring of bitches can go choke on your barking now over there on the other side, what, don't you like water? you jackals, hyenas, I'll give you such a working-over with these boots that your innards will spill out, you cannibals, NKVD[69] veterans, personal pensioners,[70] go on, bark, the more you bark, the sooner you'll croak.

All I need is to get to the opposite bank—that's all I want in this world. It's hard to keep your balance, I take every step slowly, like a heron, standing on one leg and thinking long about where to put the other foot. Behind my back the two beasts are going crazy with rage—take that! I turn around and give them the finger—and if you don't stop I'll pelt you with stones from the river bottom.

The stones on the river bank are sharp, they might tear these stage-prop boots, and then what'll I return to that guy in the orange tent? Climbing that bank is my first duty today, why else would I have come to this town? To recite poems? Drink vodka? Dance in the square?

Here's the forest, it's not very thick really, my eyes have got so used to the darkness I imagine I'm a great wild cat, a night creature in this forest. My eyes are probably glowing. On a night like this it would be nice to sit somewhere and listen to an owl hooting. Or wolves howling. Or gunshots.

"For two years, well, maybe a bit less, a year and a half, they hauled people along the old road from the Chortopil prison. I'd be lying, Hryts, if I said there weren't murdered people under every tree. There probably isn't another forest like it in the whole world. We weren't allowed to go there—they cordoned the place off and stationed guards, even a cow couldn't get through. A few cows were killed that way, but people didn't say a word for fear of finding eternal rest in that forest themselves. We thought at first that they were searching for something or setting up bunkers. At night, as soon as you heard the roar of motors from the old road—run! better hide your head under the covers and pretend you don't hear a thing, because they're coming, they're coming ..."

The forest is phosphorescent, it glows, it's lime-white, it's decaying and falling to pieces, the corpses are breaking it up from below. I'll just call them, and they'll get up. Hey, get up, all of you in white, start shining! They're standing on either side of the track stretching their arms out to me, they're saying something. Actually, they're not here. They were buried in the cemetery back in forty-one with prayers and religious songs, and a big cross with a barbed-wire wreath was erected on their mass grave, "that's why later all of our people, to a man, joined the nationalist partisans: they didn't want to fall into their hands alive."

The track is getting steeper, my feet are groaning, what am I going to find on the other side of the wood besides an empty meadow with sky above it? Is it possible that there won't even be a chimney, a beam, or a cross? Is it possible that I'll disappear in this wilderness like the last of the inhabitants, flesh of their flesh, blood of their blood? Let them all follow after me, hey, don't just stand there beside the track, come on, we'll hold a festival of the Resurrecting Spirit, we'll pray, we'll drink, we'll sing, why not, this time the terrible trucks with their red headlamps won't be coming up the old road. And they do come, they hurry after me, breathing down my back, faster, faster, this is only a little wood, we won't even have time to think before we are out of it, and then we'll be home. They are racing ahead of me, but I'll still be the first, I woke you up, I'm the one alive among you dead people, let me be the first to get home, otherwise why the devil did I come here to this place of yours?

I come out of the forest, there's light ahead, my heart is beating like a bell sunk in my chest, "at the highest point was the church, behind it, closer to the forest, the cemetery, and lower still, on the slopes, houses with fruit and vegetable gardens all the way down to the old road—not many of them, fourteen or thereabouts, Little Village was just a hamlet, but they preferred not to touch our boys, because even at the Chortopil market they could thrash all comers, they took their knives with them when they went dancing and they always married girls from other places, and your grandad couldn't teach them order, respect, or brotherly love no matter how hard he tried, he just married them off to girls from other places, that was all he could do.

In the Donbas guys also carried knives. After matriculation night we had a brawl with the technical-school kids from miners' families and I got it in the ribs, but it didn't go in very deep. Two weeks later I was better and poems started coming to me, they put themselves together in my head. At the time I never suspected that when I threw myself into a brawl, only to get stabbed with a knife, the whole of Little Village was behind me, I didn't know it then, but it saved me from the knife, me, its youngest.

Well, why have all of you stopped at the edge of the forest, unable to go another step? Like you, I'm dizzy from running, but what I see before me makes me even dizzier. Why this huge, roofless structure with black holes in it, these trenches, piles of brick, pipes, wooden window frames, and stacks of roof tiles? Why so many toilet bowls, bathtubs, and washbasins, so much sand, why these cranes and concrete mixers, surely nobody lives here, weren't they all chased by vicious dogs all the way to the railway station and packed brutally there into freight cars?

"The Hutsul Girl International Tourist Centre. Contractor: Chortopil Building Trust," it said in Russian on the sign in front of the building site. "Construction begun in 1947," thought Hryts. "Idyllic location, picturesque landscapes, close to a forest and plentiful wild strawberries, extraordinary mountain air infused with the aroma of grasses and fir trees, and in the River, whose waters are the cleanest in Europe, trout thrive. At your disposal are luxurious units with a bathroom and TV, videophones, a restaurant, a bar, a late-night bar, a casino, a swimming pool, a sauna, a discotheque, and all this for the ridiculous price of about a thousand dollars a day, peanuts. Experienced chefs will prepare countless delectable national dishes for you, and experienced young prostitutes will show you a good time. Your holiday program includes wine tastings and excursions on horseback to the mountain pass. The Golden Jews'-Harpists folk-loric ensemble will perform Hutsul melodies for you, and the young poet Hryts Shtundera with his *oseledets* will recite his verses. We await you in our hospitable land, please come!"

"From the old road, Hryts, I saw Little Village dying—not a soul remained of our people, there were just soldiers chasing the cattle out of the yards, then I could only see the church because it was at the highest point, and the carts were nearly overturning, nearly falling apart, from going at such a crazy speed because the dogs were chasing us, the dogs were leaping at the horses, where they got dogs like that I don't know to this day, and we were all silent as if at a funeral, we didn't even have the strength to spit or weep, because in the end it was we who had let them take us alive, but what could we do, there were just women, children, and a few of us fifteen-year-olds, they said they were taking us to Kherson oblast, then there were some changes and from Shepetivka we were hauled all the way to Kazakhstan."

Hryts felt the ground open beneath his feet. He was falling into an even greater darkness, but he did not call out, for this was to be a natural death—here, amidst these piles of brick, on the building site of a fabulous tourist resort, to lie down in a foundation trench and fall asleep together with the grass of his native Little Village as its youngest inhabitant, as the contemporary of those who used to take knives into the forest or to the market at Chortopil. But, getting up again, covered in sand and clay, he saw the same sky above him. The trench was shallow and he had not even hurt himself. Though it was dark he saw next to him, at the bottom, a pile of rags. He bent over and struck a match, and again was unable to call out, even though before him lay the corpse, fresh, not even cold, of a large man with a bullet hole in his head, he was somehow very familiar, no doubt because of the absence of the gold chain from his short, fat neck. Nemyrych's book proved to be missing, too. If you go in for rob-bery, do it properly.

Hryts needed a smoke. He struck a match against the sole of the dead man's shoe—exactly like Mickey Rourke in the film *Angel*

Heart—inhaled deeply several times, and started climbing out of the trench. The *oseledets* kept getting into his eyes. The night had reached its apogee.

The Brat got here some time after two, to top it off he wasn't alone but with some shaggy guy, said he was a great poet, but I had no more space because the front room was in use, so I made up my own bed, he kept asking if I was a hard-currency whore, because he had a whole ten dollars and would be able to pay me for the entire night, "but I didn't imagine you'd look like this," what a comedian, how did you imagine me, youth doesn't spring eternal. The Brat winked at me to take the ten dollars the bearded guy was waving in front of my nose, but I felt sorry for him—a drunk always gets stupid, even if he's ten times a poet it makes no difference, meanwhile the Brat went to the kitchen and began stuffing his face as usual, we stayed in the room and smoked, the bearded guy wanted to recite something off by heart but couldn't remember a thing, he roared with laughter, nearly pissed himself laughing, laughed so hard he got the hiccups, "I know, milady, that you can give me a little something to drink, Bilynkevych told me so," what a guy, calls me milady, I tell him that lords and ladies haven't been around for a while, "well then, I shall call you my darling," what a comedian, I've got a grown-up son serving in the army, "you deign to have a grown-up son?" he asked and shook with laughter even more, "but I'd guess you were no more than twenty-five," stupid liar, he can barely turn his tongue around in his mouth but doesn't stop lying, I poured him a hundred and fifty grams to shut him up but he got even more talkative, "well, when is the sweet reward?" I went to the kitchen, I knew it, the Brat had demolished nearly half a kilo of the sausage I was keeping for Pentecost, thinking Mykola Kindratovych would come, "never mind, I'll get you some more," the Brat said, I'll have to remind him tomorrow, tonight he would promise anything, meanwhile the bearded guy crashed onto the bed in his socks and was asking me to undress him, "this service should be included in the general fee of ten dollars," get lost, you with your dollars, I nearly screamed at him but I didn't, I shut up because he's drunk and stupid and young as well, I took off his socks and he stuck the ten dollars into my bra, "that's President Hamilton," he said, what a weirdo, and then he kissed my hand, I've never seen anything like it, and then, for no reason, he started crying and said he was more miserable than anybody, I felt sorry for him and went to have a wash after I put on Rotaru[71] for him, I turned out the light and went into the bathroom but the Brat was sitting there and puking, I gave him some milk of magnesia and then chased him out, he went into the front room, but none of the girls was free, so he came back to bug me again, "I'll just rub your back," he stuck to me like the clap, began getting undressed, I hit him in the snout with a wet towel, you little pest, your mother and I went to school together, I've got a son just five years younger than you, he's serving near Moscow in a construction battalion, he says in his letters that he can't take it and he's going to run away, and you've made yourself at home here, you gorge yourself on my sausages, and now you want this as part of the general fee of ten dollars, I suppose, slap across his snout, slap, slap, he put his hands up, I could see blood dripping from his nose, I felt sorry for him, but he starts up again, that bearded guy, he says, must have fallen asleep by now, "if you don't have any more room, we could all sleep in this bed, have you ever tried a three-some?" I had only ever seen that on video, but I didn't want to try it, it was shameful, I chased him into the kitchen, you can sleep on the floor, here's a blanket and a pillow, bed down on the floor, I've had enough, I'm sick of all of you, why don't you all shut up at last, it's nearly three and you're squealing like stuck pigs, I've got people resting here, one of them is a famous poet, I went into my room, the bearded guy was already asleep on my bed, he was dressed as before, only he had his socks off, I gently took off his sweater, his shirt, turned off the music, took off his trousers, he was murmuring something, "O moon, O moon, O flowers, flowers,"[72] like a baby in its sleep, he's so funny, must be around thirty, maybe a bit older, I didn't check his ID, I've got my own troubles, you've got yours, man are you drunk, lying there without moving, just purring like a tomcat, saying something I can't understand, I listened and he opened his eyes, he's looking at me, "you're probably not a day younger than forty," thirty-eight, I say, "you have the breath of a forty-year-old, young girls don't smell like that, not at all, I know," well, thank you very much for the compliment, lover-boy, should I kick you out or what, Mykola Kindratovych has been sleeping with me for nearly twenty-one years and he never said anything like that, but this guy just raves on, "in the human body those orifices above the navel are clean and those below it are unclean, but a young girl's orifices are all clean," so get out of here, go find yourself a young girl with clean orifices and leave me in peace, you show up here in the middle of the night drunk, and now you're being picky like the last whore on earth, nothing pleases him, if only you'd known me twenty years ago, all the boys were crazy about me, at dances there were bloody fights over me, and Mykola Kindratovych gave me imported stockings and flowers and chocolates and brought me home in his car from the restaurant, and I had nowhere to live so he got me a flat, that's how much they loved me, and here you are carrying on about the clean and unclean, I nearly cried, barely stopped myself, fat lot of good you are to me, you shifty poet, I've got my pride, and then he said I wasn't like the others, that I've a golden heart, he started kissing my hands, the circus clown, then I started crying and he threw himself on top of me, where did he get the energy, I thought, he's not good for anything now, but he did his bit quite well, I barely had time to figure out what was happening before he was in, "what, didn't you believe I was a poet," and only then did he fall asleep with his beard on my belly, his hair was all wet, tired as a lumberjack, he was, never said another word, sleep, sweetheart, sleep, there's plenty of time till morning, his beard looks like it's stuck on, and he really looks just like a child.

"I've had enough of this festival of yours," said Marta—not the Marta with whom Martofliak had spent the night, but Martofliak's wife. "I want to go to the hotel. Tomorrow I'm getting up early and going home."

"Why would you do that?" Nemyrych asked. "The most important part begins tomorrow."

"I've left two children at home," said Marta.

"But they're with your parents. Nothing will happen to them," Khomsky assured her.

"You're just angry at Rostyk, I can understand that," allowed Nemyrych.

Marta was unable to restrain herself: "That old half-wit, that goat!"

"All right. We'll go to the hotel. But for this we need to find our Chortopil friend. He's sleeping somewhere over there, in the Chrysler," reflected Nemyrych.

"I'll find that hotel perfectly well without him. I've been to Chortopil a hundred times."

"Well, then let's go." Khomsky took her arm.

"Fine. But we can't leave that boy sleeping in the car," insisted Nemyrych.

"What could possibly happen to him? And anyway, do we really need him?" Khomsky arched his lip contemptuously. "Old buddy, you're creating a problem where none exists. Bilynkevych is sleeping in a luxury car. He's fine. But we should be sleeping in a hotel. That's all. Let's go."

"He might have suffocated in there," speculated Nemyrych.

"All the more reason not to drag him out. Imagine, you open the trunk and there's Bilynkevych's corpse. It would spoil your evening for you," said Khomsky, trying to be convincing.

"You two can go to the hotel," Nemyrych disagreed. "I'll find Bilynkevych."

"What a wonderful idea!" said Khomsky approvingly. "So piss off, go look for him if you find him more interesting than us. As I understand it, you're leaving us on purpose because you're sick of us. I trust you remember where the Imperial is parked?"

"Not far from here," said Nemyrych.

"Nothing is far from anywhere in this town," Khoma agreed. "Listen, it's quite possible he's a queer. Be careful!"

"You've got to try everything at least once in your life, even that," Nemyrych reassured him and, with a wave of his hand, departed into the festival crowd.

The festival was already rapidly dying down, the imagination of the magicians and jokers was inexorably exhausting itself, and by now practically nothing interesting was going on in the square: just some fireworks, a pantomime with Angels and Clowns, some girls walking on their hands, except that later it turned out that these were feet, and a tall dude in the red costume of an Executioner with an axe in his belt was inviting everyone to partake of some baked sausages "of my own manufacture," as he asserted. Nemyrych bought a sausage, which seemed rather sweet to his taste, and headed for the aforementioned monument behind which the amazing prewar car should have been standing.

But the Chrysler was not there. As could be ascertained from eyewitness accounts, half an hour earlier the black limousine had lifted off from the square and, after briefly circling the town-hall tower, disappeared into the night sky over Chortopil. Instead, in the crowd Yurko caught sight of a gentleman with a video camera sporting a checked cap, glasses, and a grey beard and clad on this occasion in a good-quality black suit with gold pinstripes.

"Mr. Popel," Nemyrych greeted him, "where is your magnificent Chrysler?"

"Oh, Mr. Shtundera, I beg your pardon, Mr. Nemyrych, I am delighted to see you!" said Dr. Popel in lieu of an answer.

Yurko was not satisfied. "I wonder, did you have a look inside the trunk of your car?"

"I am taking advantage of this happy opportunity to make a souvenir video of my participation in this unforgettable festival," replied Dr. Popel.

"You see, a certain young man was supposed to be in the trunk of your car." Nemyrych was not to be distracted.

"But I prefer Japanese tapes, because German ones are not light-sensitive enough," said the doctor, continuing the conversation.

"What, can you get Japanese tapes where you come from?" capitulated Nemyrych.

"Of course, there was nothing I could do but throw him out of the trunk, because I don't like that kind of thing," said the Swiss, beginning to shed light on the situation.

"And what would a video camera like this cost, for example?" said Yurko, seeking clarification.

"You know, he went away the moment I threw him out. I don't know where he might be now. Vomiting somewhere, I'm sure," answered Dr. Popel.

"You wouldn't know where to find the Chortopil hotel?"

"I do not know the newer buildings here, and besides, I am staying with my family. It gives me great pleasure to invite you to visit their house as my guests; a grand night-long reception is about to begin there."

Nemyrych thought for a moment.

"I wouldn't be intruding?" he said hesitatingly.

"I promised that I would bring along one of the famous Ukrainian poets, most probably yourself, Mr. Nemyrych. They are preparing to receive you. And so, if you please—" and the doctor nodded in the direction they would need to take.

"They won't force me to recite poetry?" Nemyrych hesitated again once they had set off.

"They are not interested in your poems," said the doctor, dispelling his doubts. "They are only interested in the fact that you are a famous poet."

"I see," nodded Nemyrych understandingly.

They turned into the former St. John the Baptist Street and walked in silence for a while. It was the time when gates had been shut and lanterns extinguished. Most of the buildings were also dark, and only from one window the barely audible strains of a harpsichord emanated. At every step there were garbage cans and cats, or perhaps rats, in a word, animals that scurried across the road and hid in basements with broken windows. Yurko could not help admiring the ancient architecture while he tried to think of what to ask Popel. Finally he came up with something.

"Mr. Popel, did your car really take off and fly away?"

The doctor gave him an attentive look.

"My car is where I parked it when I arrived."

"Then how did that fellow end up in the trunk?" persisted Nemyrych.

"You know," began the doctor, somewhat irritated, "that is not such a simple matter. Sometimes I find it hard to know what is going on here in your country. I am, after all, a citizen of Switzerland. There are many things I do not understand about your way of life. We live in different social systems. In addition, we have a confederation, while you have a unitary state. It depends on what you prefer, I guess."

Yurko decided to drop the theme of the car and Bilynkevych, as these questions clearly aroused the doctor and made him talk nonsense instead of answering. So, after some thought, Nemyrych selected a new question from the depths of his intellect:

"How does a confederation differ from a federation?"

"I can tell you nothing about this, because I am not interested in politics at all," the doctor courteously explained.

"Mr. Popel, conversing with you is a great pleasure. Do we still have far to go?"

"That does not depend on us," the doctor mysteriously replied.

I guess he's lost his marbles, thought Nemyrych. These things do happen to psychiatrists. Or maybe he's just deaf and can't hear what I'm asking.

Whatever the case may have been, Yurko lost all desire to communicate further with the schizophrenic doctor. However, as soon as they turned off the former St. John the Baptist Street into the former King Danylo Street, the doctor spoke up.

"I ask you to be as polite as possible in this company. Do not rest your elbows on the table, do not smack your lips, do not snivel, use a knife, fork, and napkin when eating, do not belch and, pardon the expression, do not fart. The gathering will be exceptionally refined, and I shall be greatly aggrieved if you behave in an uncouth manner."

"Will there be young girls there or, shall we say, young women I can flirt with?" Nemyrych asked with impertinent interest, feeling rather stung by the doctor's admonitions concerning the rules of etiquette.

"Apropos, there is no room to spend the night, so please don't count on any such thing," answered the doctor, not at all apropos.

"Don't count on what—overnight accommodation or girls?" Yurko asked, seeking clarification.

"Count on yourself alone," replied the Swiss. Then, rubbing his hands contentedly, he said, "Everything has worked out splendidly. We have managed to discuss everything in detail. Please knock at this door, for we have arrived."

They were standing in front of an indescribably old building that somehow resembled a miniature fortress, and if Yurko had known Chortopil a little better, he would have guessed that this was the famous Gryphon Villa to which hordes of tourists were taken daily. But Yurko did not know this, and so he boldly knocked on the door.

The door was opened by a servant wearing livery with gold braid and such a stupid expression that it evoked an immediate craving to whack him between the eyes. For Nemyrych this desire was further intensified by the fact that in outward appearance the servant reminded him of some very highly placed person, only he could not figure out whom. The servant relieved the doctor of his video camera and placed it, with great deference, into a kind of niche. He then led them up a wooden staircase. The staircase, indeed the entire building, was illuminated only by candles, which were, in truth, countless. From above the strains of sweet music were audible over a background of subdued and polite conversations.

Between the ground floor and the first was a landing, and on it a seemingly unbreakable door with a lion's head instead of a handle. The servant pressed the tip of the lion's nose, and the door opened.

"Mr. Nemyrych," said the doctor, "please step into the dressing room and select a suit. You are not appropriately attired for this reception. I shall wait here."

Yurko entered a room with wardrobes and mirrors expecting to get a knife in the back, which would have been quite in keeping with the tenor of the situation, but all ended well. The wardrobes contained a great many completely identical sets of men's clothing neatly arrayed on coat hangers: a black tailcoat and trousers, a waistcoat, a white shirt, a bow tie, and under each hanger, a pair of pointed lacquered shoes. These items differed in size alone. Yurko began hurriedly to change, keeping an eye on the open door and the mirror next to it, in which he could see himself wearing nothing but his underpants. This made him feel even more vulnerable. It proved to be quite difficult to find suitable attire. If the coat fit, the trousers did not, or the shirt was about to split at the seams. Or vice versa. Time passed, and it seemed to Yurko he had already tried on half of the wardrobe without success. He began to get irritated and was looking around to see if the room had a window through which he might escape this idiotic situation, when he noticed an outfit with a note pinned to the lapel. "For Mr. Yurii Nemyrych," it read. The clothes seemed to have been tailored for him, even the lacquer shoes weren't tight, and a few minutes later Yurko saw himself from various angles in the mirror looking as he had never looked before, namely, perfect.

"You took a bit too long getting dressed," said Popel with slight reproach. "I had to dismiss the servant. He has had a very tiring day. He deserves a rest."

"Does he work here all the time?" asked Yurko when they were ascending the stairs again.

"He does not work here at all. He is the first secretary of the local Communist Party Committee. We invited him," explained the doctor.

The door on the first floor proved higher and even more massive, but it was wide open, and Nemyrych, accompanied by the doctor, stepped over the threshold into a huge candle-lit chamber. Here and there men and women in evening dress were moving about with impeccable deportment. Without a sound servants dressed, like the first, in liveries with gold braid, unobtrusively offered the guests champagne and orangeade from gilded trays. In the distance, on a little podium, Nemyrych glimpsed a quartet of musicians in frock coats and powdered wigs playing a poignant sonata for viola da gamba, viola d'amore, flute, and cembalo.

"Scarlatti," said Nemyrych, pretending recognition.

"Corelli," Dr. Popel corrected him. "But it doesn't matter."

"A wonderful rendition," judged Yurko. "Winners of some competition, I suppose?"

"Oh, no, they are local boys," Popel disappointed him again. "I should acquaint you with some of the guests."

Yurko rather clumsily picked up a glass of champagne from a passing tray, spilling a little in the process.

"Watch out," said the server in Russian, measuring him with an angry glare. "The types that come crawling around ..."

And he went on his way.

They approached a small group of ladies and gentlemen who were politely chattering about something.

"Let me introduce you," said Popel with a scarcely perceptible bow. "This is Mr. Nemyrych, the famous poet." And, his mission complete, he withdrew, bowing slightly once again.

"Oh, how delightful!" enthused a balding man with a monocle. "Harazdetsky, Gymnasium teacher," he introduced himself.

Probably the principal of the local elementary school, Nemyrych decided for himself and, transferring his glass from his right hand to his left, kissed the palm of the hand of a young lady who in the meantime was giving her name:

"Amalthea Harazdetska." She showed him a slightly bucktoothed smile.

A stout matron with a diamond collar on her marble neck also gave a fake smile and said that she was Clytemnestra Harazdetska, head of the Women's Destiny Society.

A dark-haired, elegant young man, his hair parted in a straight, thin line, bowed in a crisp military manner, clicking his heels:

"Count del Campo, aviator."

"Yurko," said Nemyrych, pressing his hand.

"I've read some of your poems, Mr. Nemyrych," Harazdetsky

informed Yurko. "I like them. They have scope, and they're very patriotic. I think you're a major talent."

"Only please don't become too captivated by that decadence business," warned Mrs. Clytemnestra Harazdetska. "Our poor nation needs courageous liberating words, not senseless playthings. What our womenfolk await from you is truthful poems about their hard lot."

"Oh, Mummy, don't be so demanding!" said Miss Amalthea, her teeth gleaming again. "After all, Mr. Nemyrych is still very young. And what do you say, Count?"

"Poetry interests me least of all," pronounced del Campo.

"Oh, but surely up there, in the heavens, divine thoughts must enter your mind?" Amalthea raised her eyebrows.

"When I am, as you put it, in the heavens, all that enters my mind is the direction of the wind and whether I have enough gasoline," said del Campo, his black eyes flashing.

Yurko was unable to contain himself and emitted a barely perceptible belch. It was the champagne. Now one of them will challenge me to a duel, he thought, but everyone pretended that they had noticed nothing, and the crisis passed.

"Jean-Baptiste Lully. Gavotte," announced one of the musicians, and the music began again.

"Tell me, Mr. Poet, were you at the Lanckorońskis' party last week?" inquired Amalthea. "I think I saw you there."

"Last week I was being evicted from my hostel," replied Nemyrych.

"So you were not at the Lanckorońskis' party?" Amalthea continued.

"I thought I had spoken plainly," said Yurko, dispelling her doubts.

"A pity," sighed Amalthea. "It turned out to be a very nice party. So it was not you who recited Rilke there?"

"Rilke?" repeated Nemyrych. "No, it wasn't. I only know Heine[73] by heart. And Kholodny."[74]

"A pity," sighed Amalthea again. "There was a poet there who recited Rilke."

"It wasn't me," said Nemyrych.

"Now I can see that it wasn't, but at first I thought that it was."

"No, it wasn't, because I don't know Rilke by heart."

"Yes, of course, it's just that you look very similar to the poet who was there."

"Very likely, because I couldn't have been there."

One could sense that for the count this dialogue—unlike the charms of Miss Amalthea—was becoming more and more irritating. He flashed his black eyes again and said dryly,

"That's all very well, poetry is a fine pastime. But what is your main profession, Mister Nemyrych?"

To satisfy his curiosity, Yurko responded, "My name is not Misternemyrych, but Nemyrych."

Amalthea let out a ringing laugh and even clapped her hands. Del Campo turned visibly sullen.

"Excuse me, I have to visit the washroom," he abruptly declared, and then departed.

"Poor Michael Scipio," said Madame Clytemnestra, "he seems to be madly in love." And she cast a playful look at her daughter, then at her husband.

"Ahem," said Mr. Harazdetsky, adjusting his monocle.

"Mummy, he is so prosaic," sighed Amalthea and, leaning toward Yurko, whispered in his ear, "Take my arm and let's go for a little walk."

They sailed away into the salon just as a musician on the podium announced,

"Christoph Willibald von Gluck. Orpheus's aria from the opera *Orpheus and Eurydice.*"

The flute began to play sweetly, and Yurko, arm in arm with Amalthea, accidentally stepped on the foot of a red-haired young man who was doing some calculations in pencil on his shirt cuff.

"Nathan Hosenduft, hides and bones," the young man introduced himself, presenting Yurko with his visiting card, on which what he had just said was written in German in Gothic letters.

Nemyrych put the card in his pocket and took the opportunity to peek into Amalthea's décolletage, which was quite pleasant to the eye.

"Is there a vacant room here somewhere?" he asked with interest.

But the young lady just laughed and wagged a finger at him.

"Shall I tell you who the guests are tonight?" she asked with bucktoothed amiability.

"Actually, I could flush all of this, but go ahead," Yurko consented without enthusiasm. And to each successive revelation by Miss Amalthea he responded with a sceptically surprised "You don't say?" or a no less ironic "Oh!"

"You have already met Mr. Hosenduft," began Amalthea. "Now please note the people inspecting the aquarium over to our left against the wall, next to the begonias, philodendrons, and other house plants. The stately gentleman with the large belly is von Zając, commandant of the Imperial Royal police. He's rather annoying and a great card cheat. The lady who is gazing with such devotion into his eyes and whom he pinches from time to time, imagining that no one can see, is his current mistress, Leocadia Vogel. She's leaning on the arm of Mr. Imre Vogel, a lawyer, her husband, and a great clown. And that graceless bony old scarecrow waving his arms about and lecturing the rest of the company on aquarium fish is Maurice Puliarka, a science teacher at the local Gymnasium."

"You don't say?" Nemyrych expressed his disbelief for the umpteenth time.

"Now please observe the endearing couple over there. They have no doubt already attracted your attention through their completely indiscreet behaviour, Mr. Nemyrych. That ostentatious miss with the hooknose and dissolute tongue is my Gymnasium classmate, Miss Bozhena Chortyk, whom my papa has been trying unsuccessfully to seduce for ages. Next to her is her permanent suitor, Baldour de Hohenhohe, a baron and a complete idiot but a brilliant huntsman and, for that reason, a favourite of the Archduke Ferdinand. He shielded him with his own body from a terrorist's bullet when the Archduke recently visited Chortopil."

"I've heard this story somewhere before," murmured Yurko.

"Now please look to your right, where, Mr. Nemyrych, you have doubtless already noticed His Eminence surrounded by several no less important personages. That ancient crone dressed in a style belonging to no later than the middle of the last century, is Mrs. Melisanda Rzewuska née Poniatowski—the sad relic of an old Polish noble family that, regrettably, is dying out, a diviner and an intriguer without compare. That man with the shaggy black hair who is so greedily quaffing champagne is the Italian consul, Signor da Pederini, who is holidaying in the Carpathians at His Eminence's invitation, and that unpleasant fat man with the sweaty armpits and the cigar in his yellow teeth is Mr. Machalski, a local millionaire and the owner of the famous Chortopil breweries."

"People don't live that long," said Nemyrych.

"I beg your pardon?" said Amalthea.

"I said that they should all have died long ago," explained Nemyrych.

"That's not very nice of you, Mr. Nemyrych," giggled Amalthea, making no effort to conceal her front teeth.

"And you too, my darling," said Yurko, playfully passing his hand over her derriere, but deriving practically no pleasure from it. They're not so very pleasant to the touch, these curves of hers, he thought, and peeked into her décolletage again, but there everything seemed to be in place.

"Nobody has ever called me 'darling' before," said Miss Amalthea, blushing ever so slightly. "You are so affectionate, Mr. Nemyrych."

"So you say there is no empty room here?" Yurko asked her firmly.

"Henry Purcell. Sarabande," announced the musician.

A slow dance began. Some dandy on mosquito legs ambled up to Amalthea and asked her to dance. The couples, about four of them, moved majestically, the dancers approached each other and moved apart, circled about their own axes, took two steps to the side, then turned their backs to one another and began everything from the beginning again. The trick was to remember the sequence of a few not especially complicated steps.

I could do that too, thought Yurko, who was beginning to get bored by this gathering of Chortopil snobs. But at that very moment Popel appeared at his side.

"A game is beginning in the next room. Do you play cards, Mr. Nemyrych?" he inquired.

"I used to be the faculty champion at preference,"[75] Yurko replied haughtily.

"Then please follow me."

Rather provokingly, Nemyrych strolled among the dancers and blew Amalthea a kiss, and then followed the Swiss into the neighbouring chamber. It contained about as many candles as the first, but was completely empty, except that in the middle there was a huge table covered with green cloth at which three players were already waiting: the aviator del Campo, Nathan Hosenduft, and the commandant of the Imperial Royal police, von Zając. Approaching the table, Yurko straightened up and, giving a military nod, presented himself:

"Del Nemyrych."

The aviator was visibly infuriated by this word combination but held himself in check, merely giving Yurko a malicious flash with his black eyes.

"Please sit down, Mr. Nemyrych," the portly von Zając said unctuously. "I've heard that you play a good hand of preference?"

"I take my holidays only at Georgian resorts," replied Nemyrych.

"Then you are a worthy partner indeed," murmured von Zając condescendingly.

Popel, who until then had observed the table while standing in silence, produced from his pocket a brand new deck of cards, wished everyone a pleasant game, and went away somewhere again.

The game began, and Yurko was out of luck from the start. He was unable to put together even the simplest hand, constantly being "short of one" or "short of two" or having to pass hopelessly. At the same time he was convinced that von Zając was very skilfully cheating—somehow he always turned out to have precisely the card that Yurko so sorely needed.

"Our poet seems to be composing his next little epic at this moment," jibed del Campo. "You are playing very carelessly, Mr. Nemyrych."

"My concentration is disturbed by the smell of petrol that you are expelling, Mr. Aviator," parried Nemyrych, greatly regretting the absence of Miss Amalthea, for the aviator now all but shat himself with rage.

"Gentlemen, there is no point in spoiling each other's good mood," said von Zając genially, writing his latest points onto the score sheet.

Hosenduft sat in silence, his fingers drumming a Jewish melody on the table.

The game was beginning to excite Yurko, but he was getting nowhere. In addition, it was the custom here to converse about matters that bore no relation to the game, and that distracted him.

"What do you make of the most recent events in Bosnia, gentlemen? Does it not seem to you that the German ministers are trying to keep their hands clean of what might become a rather delicate situation?" von Zając asked, maintaining his stand.

"They have their reasons," disagreed del Campo, refusing to back down.

"But the whole thing might be most deleterious to our state interests," continued von Zając.

"The whole thing is deleterious in the first instance to the interests of Nicholas II and his Balkan policy, and therefore is good for us," insisted del Campo.

"And what do you say to this?" von Zając asked Nemyrych.

"It doesn't concern me greatly," replied Yurko, "but I think you're overacting a bit, boys. I know it's carnival, it's fun and games, but all these retro variants of yours are ceasing to be funny, guys. Furthermore, you, Mr. Commandant, have excessively well-trained hands, which allow you repeatedly to produce from the air precisely the card that I desperately need. You've doubtless been on study trips to the Moscow railway stations?"

And suddenly he realized that this game was more than just a game—it was a game for his life. This thought occurred to him for no particular reason, but he immediately found a whole series of corroborations. First, these conversations, which initially had seemed artificial and silly. Second, the extraordinary ease with which he kept losing. Third, these ghoulish movements of his partners, this deathly pallor of their faces, this blood drying at the corners of their mouths.

"What did you mean by that?" shouted del Campo, springing to his feet and transfixing Yurko with an otherworldly glare.

Nemyrych felt beads of cold sweat cover his forehead and back. But Miss Amalthea materialized beside the table and seized his hand.

"Let's go," she said.

"George Frideric Handel. Passacaglia," came an announcement from the next room.

"You're done for," hissed del Campo, although there was no sibilant in any of these words.

Yurko stood up on legs that felt strangely feeble and, holding Amalthea's hand, followed her out. His partners remained at the table, as though waiting for a new victim.

Amalthea led Nemyrych quickly, almost at a run, through ever new rooms of the Gryphon Villa. Yurko was feeling worse and worse: his mouth was terribly parched, his heart was beating insanely, his hair was damp with cold sweat, and before his eyes purple circles and black lightning bolts shimmered.

"Soon, my love, soon," whispered Amalthea voluptuously, but he neither wanted nor would be able to screw her, and furthermore he felt in the palm of his hand not the delicate hand of a girl, but something more like a log-end or, perhaps, the stump of an amputated limb.

The rooms rushed past with cinematic speed, ever new doors swung open, toward them flew ever new mirrors, candles, thickets of house plants, portraits in gold frames, wings, cloaks, hats, robes, stuffed birds. And when it seemed that this horrible flight would have no end and that the flood of Handel's Passacaglia, rising ever higher, was its funereal accompaniment, the final door opened at last and Amalthea pulled him into a dark, bare, and cold room with dirty grey walls and an unwashed, red-stained wood floor.

In the middle was a table of about the same size as the one in the card room, but covered with a black cloth. A single candle was burning at the very edge. Mr. Popel was dressed in a monk's cassock, and for some reason on his head he wore a bishop's mitre, which, however, was turned back to front. His hands piously folded, he was muttering some kind of prayer. His face was turned toward an indistinct picture that hung on a distant wall. Around him, in speechless devotional ecstasy, several servants in livery stood motionless, while another held a small black billygoat in his arms.

"Our lord, who art there, what thou shalt give, give us this day, from 'neath the earth, from 'neath the rocks, from 'neath the seas give us this day, shade there drowneth, drowneth there, give us sweat, give us blood, give us tears and a cart of hay, his body, his soul, his heart, his arse, from 'neath the seas, from 'neath the earth, from 'neath the rocks. Amen. In the name of the tail and the loin and the blue phallus. Amen. In the name of the spit and the blood and the sore tooth. Amen. In the name of the kidney and the gut and the eternal fear. Amen. Margadon, Beelzebub, Lucifer! Gynekhoshe, Iblis, Calvin! Asmodeus, Zoroaster, Basavriuk!"[76.]

Having completed his prayer, Mr. Popel turned to Yurko in all his grandeur. His eyes glowed with a yellow light. Yurko lay on the table covered with the black cloth. Above him the servant with the goat in his arms was flourishing a sharpened knife at the goat's neck. On the other side stood Amalthea, only not as she had been, but old and stooped, in threadbare miserable rags and with gold fangs protruding where her charming buckteeth had been.

"Take the oath," said the doctor.

… and you knew that you must cross yourself, but you did not know how to, and you shouted, Yurko, you managed to get to your feet and you tore your way out as if through cotton wool sticky with blood, through this air, and you smashed a window pane with your shoulder, and you kicked at the servant who had grabbed you by the coattail, but instead your foot hit cotton wool that was even stickier, and you leapt down, Yurko, into the chasm that is called a May night, and you fell downward for a million years, surviving all civilizations and catastrophes, all eras, and you fell straight onto some damp bushes, painfully bruising and scratching yourself in the fall, but you got up, and took another look at Gryphon Villa, and ran through the garden, and vaulted over the fence, while up above an invisible Chortopil nightingale warbled its song of passion.

And it will be almost six in the morning when at last you find your way out of the labyrinth of the town's streets and, shivering with cold, stumble upon that accursed hotel. A strange lame figure will swim toward you out of the dawn mist, and you will barely recognize Hryts with his *oseledets* and his soiled and sweaty Sich Rifleman's uniform. And you will barely say a word to each other, you will simply go into the hotel, and when you're already going up to the second floor, where a warm room and a king-size bed and hot water await you, Hryts will yawn and you'll hear him say,

"Might be a good idea to turn in for a while, eh?"

He was the kind of ordinary night-time street junkie that you see too many of shambling about at this time of night. He emerged like a sleepwalker from a deep gate that Marta and Khomsky were just passing. The junkie was barefoot. He walked lightly and gracefully two paces behind them, waving his arms like wings. He seemed to be flying, barely touching the hard Chortopil pavement. He was still feeling good, although he already knew that even the best high is transient. He was no more than seventeen, and he had blond hair.

"Why is he following us?" Marta whispered anxiously.

"How far are we from the hotel?" Khomsky asked her.

"About ten minutes," she replied, looking around.

The junkie resembled a dancer. He was dressed in a striped sweater and very baggy trousers that made him feel free and relaxed. He was flying.

"Do you want me to bash his face in?" asked Khoma.

"But he hasn't done anything to us," Marta objected.

"He's getting on my nerves. I want him to get lost."

"There's no need yet, Khoma. I'm sorry for him—he's very young."

"He needs his horns broken off, that's all," argued Khomsky.

"Maybe we should walk faster and let him fall behind?"

They quickened their step, but the junkie did not fall behind. He beat his winged arms with greater force and was once again two paces behind them.

"I told you there was only one way out," Khomsky insisted.

"But he hasn't touched us," Marta objected again.

"When he touches us it'll be too late. I won't hit him, I'll just say a few words."

"He won't understand a thing."

"He will. I'll tell him to get lost or he'll get it in the neck."

"Orest dear, maybe we can make it to the hotel without that? I don't think he can even see us, so what's the point of talking to him? Right now he's high as a kite and he simply doesn't see us."

"Stop and don't move!" shouted the junkie, proving Marta wrong.

They stopped. Marta realized she was trembling. Khomsky turned sharply about and took a step toward the junkie.

"Young man, were you bleating to us?" he asked, rippling his jaw muscles and pulling his hands out of his coat pockets.

"Oh, young man!" laughed the junkie. "Young man!"

"Listen carefully, buddy." Khoma was speaking as firmly as he could, but kindly at the same time. "I really don't like you following us. The town is big enough at night. Go wherever you like, but leave us alone."

"Buddy!" laughed the junkie.

"What are you trying to say?"

"Old man, you're crazy." He said "crazy" in English.

"You know, I don't have to talk to you like this," Khoma assured him, much colder now.

"Orest dear, let's go," begged Marta.

"You're crazy, crazy!"

"Get lost, you hear?" Khoma took Marta by the arm and walked on.

But the junkie did not get lost. He laughed and pretended to be chasing them, but maintained his distance of two paces throughout. Khomsky stopped and turned to him again.

"Don't", said Marta.

"What do you mean, 'don't'?" asked the junkie. "What do you mean, 'don't'? You're a crazy woman. You're going the wrong way. I know you. I've fucked you!"

"There you are," said Khomsky, affecting an apathetic and bored tone, "and you said 'don't.' Now I have no choice."

"And you!" shouted the junkie, "you, old man! Hit me right here." He pointed to his chest. "Hit me. Do you understand, you old goat?"

He spread his arms like one crucified, or, more precisely, like a scarecrow. He smelt of something very unpleasant, and his lips were covered in cold sores.

"Hit me, come on, hit me," he all but begged. "See, I'm right here."

"I really should put my boot through your teeth," snarled Khomsky, "especially for calling me an old goat. But I don't want to spill your stupid blood. I'm letting you go."

"Nah," laughed the junkie again. "You're not an old goat. You're a faggot, got that? I know you, you're from School Number Eight. Faggot!"

"Marta dear, would you please walk ahead a little?" said Khomsky gently.

"Marta dear, would you please suck me off?" mocked the junkie.

"Khoma, please, let's go, how long does this have to go on?" Marta was frightened since this was no longer a joke. But she did move off about ten paces.

The junkie dropped his arms and raised one leg.

"Hit me," he asked again. "See, I'm standing on one leg."

"Buddy," said Khomsky, conciliatory again, "I suspect you're a karate expert. And all in all you're a great guy. Go your own way."

"Aha!" shouted the punk. "Go my own way! You're pissing yourself you're so scared!"

He took a sideways leap and struck a warlike pose.

"Do you want me to pull a knife?" he asked.

"A knife—that's nice," said Khomsky.

"Check it out!" and he really did produce a small knife from somewhere inside his baggy trousers.

"What a beautiful knife," Khoma assured him. "Where did you get it? Let me have a look."

"Ha! A beautiful knife! Here!"

Khoma held the knife in his hand, pretending to examine it. Then he asked, "What's eating you, buddy?"

"I want to kill you all," explained the junkie.

"Who is 'you all'?"

"All you old goats and faggots. Like you."

"Are you from Chortopil?"

"I know everybody here, understand?"

"I believe you. Do you have a smoke?"

"Orest!" called Marta. "Let's go, how long can this last?"

"Just a moment. Sorry, buddy, I have to go—there's a lady waiting for me."

"I'm letting you go," said the junkie. "Go. That's your whole trouble, go, you miserable faggot."

Khomsky kicked him unexpectedly in the stomach. Marta screamed, the youth gave a hollow croak and bent over. Khoma threw the knife into the grass. Then, clamping his hands together, he brought a double fist down hard on the other's head. But the junkie did not fall, as Khomsky had expected. He jumped aside several paces and shouted,

"Far out! Why did you wait so long?"

Then and there he picked up from the ground a large stone that, God knows why, was lying there. Khoma went to kick him again, intending to knock the stone out of his hand, but he missed and then had to run. He grabbed Marta by the hand. The boy ran after them, stone in hand.

"Aaargh!" he screamed. "Death! Death to you all!"

Their legs were giving out, and it seemed that the junkie would catch up with them any second. He threw the stone at them when he was five metres away, but Khoma managed to react and duck in time. The stone flew over his head. Khoma stopped.

"Marta, you go ahead," he gasped and went at the junkie again.

Blood was trickling from the junkie's mouth. Khoma had evidently booted him hard in the gut.

"You're crazy, crazy," the junkie was saying, this time in a different, pathetic voice, while gradually falling back. "What did you do that for? You're stupid. I never did anything to you, you old goat."

And suddenly he burst into tears, turned his back on Khomsky, and limped away holding his side. Khomsky stopped and watched him go. He was walking faster and faster, sniffling and wiping his face with his hand. Soon he disappeared into the darkness, although that "crazy, crazy, crazy" of his continued to echo inside Khomsky for some time.

The Blue Mountain Hotel was quite nearby, lit up like a giant luxury liner unable to sail for the ocean out of this accursed trap in the mountains. The Blue Mountain Hotel was awaiting its late arrivals.

Martofliak woke up from the sensation that some object was falling on him from above—not so much a rock as a bag full of warm dough—and that object was threatening to crush him beneath its suffocating weight. On opening his eyes he could not divine the cause of the nightmare straight away, but gradually he came to the conclusion that under the circumstances he could scarcely have dreamt of anything else. He was sleeping with a woman he did not know and about whom he could say almost nothing, except that she was naked and quietly snoring. Her heavy right breast was resting on Martofliak's collarbone, quite close to his throat, so the dream could indeed have ended in suffocation. Freeing his numb right leg from between her sweaty thighs, Martofliak discovered to his astonishment that he, too, was naked, but he decided to make no connection between this and the nakedness of his neighbour. He hesitantly raised his head, looked around in the room's grey pre-dawn light, and then the glimmer of a recollection came to him. His clothes, including his underwear, were strewn around the bed. The bed turned out to be very wide, and in it, on the side opposite from him, a third person was sleeping. It was Bilynkevych, who, admittedly, was fully clothed and even had his shoes on. The name tag with "ORGANIZ-ING COMMITTEE" written on it fluttered on his chest as he breathed deeply and evenly.

He felt lousy. He wanted some beer. He wanted to know what all this meant and what he should do next. Martofliak walked around the bed, trying at least to see who and how old she was, but the woman was sleeping so that her face was invisible from all directions.

Martofliak dressed, tiptoed out of the room, and, with surprising ease, found the bathroom and toilet. He caught sight of himself in the mirror and grimaced—less from the sight of his protruding lobster eyes and the bags beneath them than from the realization of the full depth of his fall. He yawned and washed his eyes. The sight of water pouring from the tap aroused his thirst, and for a long time he pressed his mouth to the cold, foul-tasting stream.

There were two rooms in the apartment. The other one proved to be much larger than the one in which he had spent the night. He went in there in quest of a mouthful of beer or a cigarette. About twelve people were asleep in the room, not only on the beds but also on the floor, among empty bottles and a mess of carnival costumes. They seemed to have fallen asleep at the height of arousal, having clambered onto one other and then passed out in fantastic poses. The overflowing ashtray reeked, but Martofliak found in it a rather fat butt, which he lit. There was no beer.

There could be no doubt about it: he was in a bordello. A contemporary, very low-grade Soviet bordello. A sleeping, early-morning bordello where men become as helpless as children and, having conscientiously worked all night to satisfy their purchased ladies, collapse exhausted into the dawn mist. And then it seems that the main thing for which they have come here is not to make love, but the possibility of sleep, this two-hour impenetrable, early-morning sleep during which one could rob, butcher, or suffocate them, and they would not even move, being at this moment somewhere far, far away. Their sleep is dedicated and inspired, they sleep with their whole being, unsparing of their lives, unselfishly and completely. After all, at any moment some bastard might wake them up and send them to the front or, perhaps, to dig trenches or build a narrow-gauge railway. That's why every minute is precious—you have to sleep while you can, while the dawn is still breaking, while all the officers and guards in the world are asleep.

Martofliak walked gingerly out onto the stairs. The building was old, indeed ageless, the stairs creaked beneath his feet, a gust of cold air blew in through the broken window between floors, and Martofliak involuntarily shuddered. It was growing light outside. The street was empty and silent. The festival had gone to sleep for two hours, the festival was resting. Martofliak yawned again and slowly wandered off to look for the square or his hotel, or simply a booth where they might pour him a glass of beer, or his wife, or some other such thing.

It didn't hit me until I reached my room, I went into hysterics, I could only repeat, "enough, I've had enough," and Khoma stroked my head and kissed my hands, I think he still had the smell of that poor boy's blood on him, I even checked the toes of his shoes to see if they were bloody, but they were clean, Khoma brought me some water, it's all because of him, I was saying, it's all Martofliak's fault, he left me, the scum, he abandoned me, I don't interest him, I don't know how to talk about his poems, and he has such a craving for compliments, the people he likes best are the ones who sing the sweetest about his talent and his genius, and I can never praise him enough, though I know almost everything of his by heart and he's my favourite poet, I've even taught the children a lot of his dumb poems, poor kids, why do they have to put up with such a father, I fired all of this at Khoma, and he just stroked my hands and begged me to be calm, he said Martofliak was sure to return, that life was beautiful and that tomorrow morning we would have a nice breakfast, then we would go to the market and he, Khomsky, would buy me a Hutsul necklace, and then we would listen to some rock music at the foot of Painted Rock, his good friends would be playing there, "you have no idea, Marta dear, how good they are, these Doctor Tahabat kids, they set my words to music, they're a supergroup," all you know about is yourselves, all of you, I said to him, who cares if they set your words to music, he agreed, he didn't mean that they were the best musicians just because they used his words, he pulled out of his bag a bottle of champagne he had brought from Leningrad, I had almost calmed down and I wanted some champagne, but I asked him to wait, I looked at my watch, after four, Lord, my face is all swollen with tears, my mascara has run, why didn't you tell me, Khoma, "I didn't want to upset you," he was sitting in an armchair, he's so long-limbed and limber, all of him seems to be woven out of tight muscles, he has a thin manly face, hair gathered in a ponytail, I remembered the kick he gave that deviant, that night angel, where did he come from, poor child, but Khoma didn't want to bash him, he did all he could, now he's sad, he's sitting in the armchair and probably thinking about that madman but he was protecting me, protecting my honour, sit for a bit longer, I said to him and went into the bathroom, the hot water helped, I calmed down completely, things aren't so bad after all, I thought, and I looked at myself, at my body, in the mirror, I washed off those dumb tears and asked myself if just once in my life I'd be able to act, maybe wickedly, but to act, am I doomed to the end of my days to feel that I'm just the shadow of that bearded scarecrow, that narcissistic fool, and at first these thoughts frightened me, but they were enjoyable, too, something was responding inside me that I didn't know existed, and I combed my wet hair for a long time, and the hot water smelt like the lianas of the South Seas, until I was aware of every cell of my body, don't, don't, sit a little longer, I'll come out in a moment and we'll drink your champagne, and I began to hurry, because nothing could have been worse than remaining here alone till morning in this unfamiliar room listening if Martofliak is staggering up the hallway drunk and going to the window time after time to look at the empty street below, I dared myself, I didn't put on my jeans and sweater, just my dressing gown over my naked body, I'd taken it out of my suitcase, and Khoma noticed everything straight away, I heard his voice tremble, I sat down beside him, he grabbed the champagne, but his hands weren't obeying him, why are you carrying on with this tomfoolery I wanted to say, I don't want that champagne at all, but he was already struggling with the bottle, cracking some hopeless jokes, could they all be like this, these licensed Casanovas, and I decided to help him, I leaned over toward him, he thought at first that I wanted to help him with the champagne, but I said "forget the bottle," I dispelled his last doubts, and he proved to be imaginative, I managed to get to the switch, and then the dream began, I could hardly believe that this was me, I seemed to be outside myself, watching, I was tearing my way into his clothes and throwing them in all directions, he was thin and strong with very sensitive skin and ingenious hands, he tensed up at once but proved to be patient and restrained, his play was inventive, and I found out for the first time that something like this exists, but the main thing was that the main thing was still ahead, and he skilfully delayed it, and that was the greatest pleasure, that everything was still ahead, and he understood that so acutely, his long trained legs knew as much as his hands, his belly was barely damp and gave off a slight scent, I untied his hair and it fell across his shoulders, I wandered over his body, remembering to be patient and that the main thing was still ahead, but I could already feel the most inexpressible pleasure, and he heard my voice, I didn't want this at all, but my voice could no longer remain inside me, and then I heard his voice, we seemed to be calling each other from somewhere in that heaven where we were yet to be, he understood my every hint, corrected every uncertainty, nobody had understood me like this, I shuddered like agony itself, I flowed like a river, my body became a wave, I begged him to enter and begin, but he continued his play, I let him, because I understood

M's night

that if he wanted it, that was the way it had to be, he knows every-thing better than I do, and truly, he brought me to complete oblivion, I no longer knew what was where, I was complete, my body be-came indivisible, this could not go on, I seized him with both hands, I drew him in, and only then did he give way and start doing what I begged for, because I was ready to think he was being cruel, but I also believed he was not, and now this was almost the peak, I was afraid of not making it to the peak, and he had lost control over himself, that is when I vanquished him, he had forgotten the rules of his game, he no longer belonged to himself but only to me, and now it was I who was trying to restrain him, hold on a bit longer, hold on a bit longer, I couldn't hear my own voice any more, but I heard the hammering at the door, this was a catastrophe, I fell with-out reaching the peak, I fell for as long as I could hear Martofliak's hammering and his voice, but he reached it nevertheless, and I was glad of this, that at least one of us had been there, on the peak, I had given him this joy, he had reached it, he rubbed himself gratefully against me like a faithful dog, and I just kept repeating, "what are we going to do, what are we going to do …"

"Oh, greetings, pal. What are you doing in my room?" inquired Martofliak with a smile when Khomsky opened the door.

"You know," answered Khomsky, letting him in, "Marta was very worried about you. I had to calm her."

"I see," nodded Martofliak, looking around the room. "That's real charity. That's nice. And I imagined at first that they had booked you in here as a third guest."

"All sorts of things happen at these hotels," said Khomsky, shrug-ging his shoulders.

Martofliak sat down in the armchair.

"By the way, where is she?" he asked finally.

"Who?" replied Khoma.

"Marta."

"She's having a bath."

Martofliak got up and walked to the bathroom door.

"Marta dear, my love, I'm back!" he announced. "Can you hear me?"

Energetic splashing could be heard in the bathroom. Marta really was taking a bath.

Martofliak came back into the room.

"Got a smoke?" he asked.

"I'm right out, unfortunately."

"This always happens," sighed Martofliak, getting another butt out of his pocket. "We can both smoke this. Shall I leave you some?"

Khoma nodded.

"A grave-digger wouldn't smoke this stuff," said Martofliak, inhaling and coughing. "What's the time?" And he replied himself: "Half past five. Great."

"Your watch is a bit fast," said Khoma.

"Possibly."

They sat in silence for a while. Martofliak passed Khoma his butt and suddenly asked,

"Listen, why didn't you hide under the bed or something?"

"You've got stupid things on your mind, old buddy," laughed Khomsky.

"No, just imagine: you hide under the bed or, say, in the closet. Marta and I go to sleep for a bit and you leave quietly. Classic vaudeville, eh?"

"You're barking up the wrong tree," said Khomsky lightheartedly. "Do you want some champagne?"

"Pour it out," nodded Martofliak.

On this occasion the bottle opened easily and almost soundlessly. Khoma poured out half a glass each.

"Listen," asked Martofliak after a few gulps, "in tomorrow's program, or today's, for that matter, because tomorrow is only a different name for today, is there any such thing as a cuckolds' parade? You wouldn't happen to remember?"

"No," Khomsky replied seriously, "why?"

"Well, I could take part in it," explained Martofliak, putting his glass down on the coffee table.

Khoma also put his glass down and at that moment received a hefty punch in the jaw. This was so unexpected that he lost his balance and fell flat on his back.

Now they'll kill each other, thought Marta, the cause of the fray, listening from the bathroom. She grabbed her towel and began drying herself as quickly as she could, hoping to prevent such a finale.

Khomsky's lip was bleeding.

"Sorry, old buddy," said Martofliak, "I didn't mean to hit you so hard."

He stretched out his hand and Khoma got up, shaking his head like a boxer after a knockdown.

"What's going on?" said Marta, coming into the room in the very same dressing gown. She smelt of soap and water.

Martofliak politely kissed her hand.

"Will you have some champagne?" he asked.

They sat down around the coffee table, and Martofliak poured a third glass.

"Drink it," he said, giving it to Marta, "it's good after a bath."

"Have you been fighting?" asked Marta.

"Yes," replied Martofliak with animation, "and do you know what's interesting? Khoma is very strong. But I suppose you know that. He's very strong, but he didn't do a thing to me. It was I who beat him up."

"I simply couldn't hit you," said Khomsky, stemming the flow of blood from his lip with a handkerchief.

"Well!" smiled Martofliak. "You're a good friend. Loyal. I want to drink to you. Marta, let's drink to Khoma. May he soon get married, damn him!"

They clinked glasses, and Martofliak winked at her.

"Where have you been, for heaven's sake?" asked Marta, after drinking a sip.

"At a certain lady's place. Except that I don't know whether I screwed her or not. Strange story, isn't it?"

"This is very dangerous, Martofliak," said Marta.

"What is?" asked Martofliak. "The fact that I've told you about it?"

"The fact that you don't remember. What if she had VD?"

"Anything's possible," sighed Martofliak. "I was joking, of course."

"That's what I thought."

"Well, there we are, then. Hey, Khoma, why are you so miserable? The bleeding has stopped. Say something," said Martofliak, gazing at Khomsky in hope and expectation.

The latter took the handkerchief away from his mouth. There was a small red stain on it.

"I envy you, old buddy," he said.

"That's nice, but why, dammit?"

"You're a lucky man."

"I see," drawled Martofliak knowingly. "That's an entirely different matter. You want to hear a joke? A man comes home from a business trip and, naturally, catches his wife in the act."

Then he fell silent.

"Is that all?" asked Marta.

"No, it's not, but I realized that you'd heard this one already. Or perhaps one like it. They're all the same, all about one and the same thing. Maybe we should sleep a bit?" He yawned.

"There's no point," said Khomsky, shrugging his shoulders. "It's easier to sit out the couple of hours that remain. Then we can go to the market. Or somewhere else."

"That's true. There's no point," agreed Martofliak, lying down on the floor. "I'll just lie down. With my eyes open."

Silence pressed upon them like a stone. Nobody said another word. Martofliak lay face up on the floor. He really did keep his eyes open. Khoma made himself comfortable in the armchair and warmed the unfinished glass of champagne in his hand. Marta sat down on the bed and stared out of the window. It was already getting light, the first morning birds from unknown lands were beginning to sing. You could hear the slightest sound in the sleeping hotel: somebody's steps muffled by the carpet in the hallway, a key turning in the door opposite, water running in the room next door. The world had chased them and caught them.[77] They were all caught in this silence of the hotel as if in a trap.

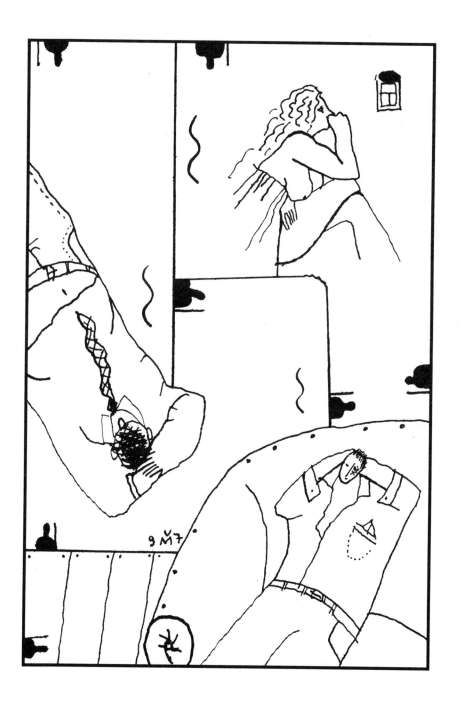

But this did not last long. Suddenly there was a noise at the door, which was now unlocked, and two monsters broke into the room. One had on a Sich Rifleman's uniform and an *oseledets* on his shaven head, the other was in black tails and a bow tie. Both of them were very crumpled, pale, and garrulous.

"Aha, the Freemasons are all present and accounted for!" shouted Hryts, greeting the company.

"Listen, Khoma," said Nemyrych, gesticulating wildly, "I met the characters from your story. There was a whole bunch of miscreants. I barely got away!"

"Sit down, guys," Martofliak answered in a flat voice from the floor. "Or bring another two glasses from your rooms. Or give us a smoke. Or sit down and be quiet. Or get the fuck out of here."

Hryts firmly chose one of the proposed variants and soon returned with two glasses. Khomsky poured out the remainder of the champagne.

"Each of us spent last night in his own way and to his own satisfaction," said Martofliak, standing up and raising his full glass. "But let it belong to each of us individually. To each his own night. I want to drink to that, friends. By the way, only you can come to the rescue with some cigarettes."

"Fat chance," replied Hryts to this.

"No way," added Nemyrych in solidarity.

"Well, if we have no cigarettes, the only thing we can do is die," sighed Martofliak, but checked himself, remembering Nemyrych.

"Shame on us," agreed Hryts.

They drank up and fell silent again. It seemed that this room was cursed by silence. Even if another two dozen poets had piled into it, they too would have become silent, and each would have stared blankly into his own corner, into his own night. The night stood behind each one's back, deep and black.

"Let's go wake Matsapura," said Khomsky, finally recovering the gift of speech.

"What room is he in?" asked Marta.

"Can you imagine, we still haven't caught up with Matsapura," continued Khomsky. "He organized this entire mess, and now he's hiding."

"He invented this crazy festival, and now he's crawled under the covers head and all and is lolling around in there," added Nemyrych.

"He summons us by telegram, tears us away from urgent business, disturbs our peace, then stuffs himself full of sausages and goes into hibernation," agreed Martofliak.

"He's making money on this festival, and we, cheap little boys that we are, allow ourselves to be bought and show up," said Hryts angrily.

"He makes money on everything."

"He's a talented guy, but a real shit."

"He always behaves this way."

"He's using us for his experiments."

"I never liked him."

"He's rather uncouth, but he has a lot of natural gifts."

"He'll come to a bad end."

"He'll be hanged for devouring human flesh."[78]

"Let's wake him," concluded Khomsky.

"I'll ring his number," announced Hryts, pulling a notebook from his pocket. "He's staying in ..."

Hryts dialed a number, but put the receiver down after a minute.

"No answer?" guessed Martofliak.

"You're so perceptive," replied Hryts.

"He's probably not in," said Nemyrych, extrapolating further still.

"Or he's too lazy to answer the phone," surmised Khomsky.

"Or he's in bed with a girl," speculated Martofliak.

"Or lying there with his throat cut," said Hryts, his face lighting up.

"Or sitting on the toilet."

"Or hanging from the chandelier."

"Or he's blocked his ears with cotton wool."

"Or he's covered the phone with a pillow."

"Do you hear?" asked Marta, who had been listening for some time to noises outside the window.

And then they heard, they really did hear, somewhere out there, in the streets of Chortopil, down below, beneath them, bursts of machine-gun fire, individual shots, the sound of feet running, the roar of motors, indistinct shouts. They rushed to the window and saw several trucks in front of the hotel. Leaping out of them were soldiers in full gear and helmets carrying automatic rifles and gas masks and wearing camouflage uniforms. They were quickly forming up in small groups and running down the adjacent streets. The officers were dispensing shrill, abrupt commands.

"What a pretty sight," said Martofliak.

The door flew open as though it had been kicked. Into the room strode a lieutenant, still very young, with an implacable facial expression. Behind him stood a two-metre-tall paratrooper holding an automatic.

"Everybody out, line up in the street," said the lieutenant in Russian.

"That is a fine idea on the whole, pal," agreed Martofliak, "but why the hell would we do that?"

"Shut it!" the lieutenant cut him off. "It's an order from the garrison commander. Everyone is to line up in the street!"

"You and your commedyander can piss off," yawned Khomsky.

"Otherwise I have the power to take special measures," said the lieutenant firmly.

"Wait, tell us what's happened, we can't just get up and go," said Martofliak, changing his tone.

"Everyone line up in the street," repeated the lieutenant, a note of fatigue in his voice. "There will be an important message from the authorities."

"And what about the General Declaration of Human Rights?" inquired Nemyrych maliciously.

"Enough!" exploded the lieutenant. "Get out immediately and line up! Enough! Your time is up!"

Out on the street they were lined up in two rows right in front of the hotel. Within ten or fifteen minutes the paratroopers had completely cleared the hotel of festival guests—sleepy, half-dressed, in multicoloured carnival rags—and marched them off in the direction of Market Square.

"No straggling, no straggling, hurry up!" the sergeants who were walking alongside commanded, as they poked the laggards with their rifles. They were almost running—the Angels, Saracens and Cossacks and all the others—they had no idea what had happened, but they were being prodded with rifles, they had been pulled from their warm morning beds, and now they were being marched somewhere, perhaps to receive a lecture on civil defence, perhaps to be shot. Nobody knew a thing.

"They've probably declared martial law," whispered Martofliak, gasping for breath.

Marta was walking beside him terrified, the same dressing gown covering her naked body.

"I'm scared," she said. "What's happening to our children?"

"There's no point despairing before we have to, we don't know anything yet," said Martofliak, trying to calm her.

"I didn't want to come here, why did I come?" lamented Marta.

"At least we have the opportunity of dying on the same day," said Martofliak.

"Hey, fella, why don't you demob?" shouted Nemyrych to one of the soldiers.

But all the answer he got was a hard thump in the back. Hryts wanted to respond in kind to teach the snotnose not to flail his arms around, but Nemyrych grabbed him with all his strength and held him tight.

"Don't touch the shit, Hryts," he said. "They're milksops, they haven't seen any service, the scumbags, the greenhorns, the latrine scrubbers!"

Khomsky alone seemed unperturbed as he obediently kept walking in step with a young Catholic priest.

It had long been light in the streets, and everyone could see how many soldiers were swarming over the city. All the side streets were blocked by trucks and armoured personnel carriers. Hryts was grinding his teeth and making fists.

"It's all shit, shit once again," he kept repeating.

They've taken over everything in the world: the telegraph, the post office, bridges, banks and hotels, they've seized the Kremlin and the Hermitage and all the other strategic buildings, they've got tanks and ammo, the operation was carried out with lightning speed with the aid of chemical weapons and barbed wire, they've taken the keys to the prisons and psychiatric hospitals, they've caught us like naked men in a bathhouse, in two or three hours they've taken all control, now they'll finally be able to restore order and declare their yearned-for war on the rest of the planet, they'll order us to lie face down on the pavement, and then they'll issue commands to "stand up, get down," and we'll get up, and then lie down again as ordered, after all they've seized Kyiv and Lviv and even Zaporizhzhia, and all in the course of some two or three hours, someone has thought this out very thoroughly, someone will get the Gold Star, they're everywhere now, they've even turned the Museum of Ukrainian Art into a jail and the cathedral into a guardhouse, and there's nothing we can do, Marta, my little one, at best I can let the bullets meant for you pass through me, that's all, and let the boys fend for themselves as best they can, after all, the firing squad isn't such a bad death for a poet, alas, what irreplaceable losses for our national literature, another executed renaissance,[79] that's how our descendants will write about us, if they ever let us have descendants, for they have great experience in purging us of descendants, that's their main business, their main goal, what a stupid ending, I didn't mean to hurt you, Marta, I won't be able to tell you anything now, about Khoma, who is in love with you, about Hryts, born in Karaganda, or about Yurko, whose last year of life they're taking away, or two at most, but I'm proud I'm here now, together with these guys, that they're going to throw us into one huge hole together with these Jews, Whores, and Gypsies, I am proud to have known these dudes, they are wonderful poets, and the chief proof of that will be the way they die, it's always like this, and what's the point of living if they've set up a communications hub in your favourite coffee house and a missile range in seventh heaven, what's the point of living if they're going to read our souls with their radars and summon us at six in the morning to wash their filthy latrines; it would be far wiser not to live to see this, I should provoke one of them, say, spit in this fellow's face, he'll lose control and empty the clip in his automatic rifle, because he knows about military honour, in this world only the command of a superior officer is more sacred than that, I would do this trick right away, except that first I have to let the bullets meant for you pass through my body, I can't delegate that to Khomsky even though he loves you, but your hand is in mine, it has been a long time since we held hands, the last time was seven years ago when you were pregnant with little Oksana and drew my portrait in lipstick on all the mirrors in our house.

On Market Square you were formed up into rows with your backs to the sun, which had risen above the town hall. There were very many of you—hundreds, who, like you, had come to revel at the festival of the Resurrecting Spirit. You were silent as you watched the officer pacing in front of you, glancing at his wristwatch and looking expectantly up the former Street of the Sisters of the Sacrament. The town-hall flag had been lowered.

You, Martofliak, were holding your wife's hand as your last refuge in this world, you, Yurko, were licking your dry lips and softly whistling something to yourself, you, Hryts, were recalling your last poem, which you had not yet managed to write down, and you, Khomsky, were drawing something on the pavement with the toe of your shoe, but it was no good, your shoe was leaving no marks.

At seven o'clock on the dot a lovely armoured personnel carrier drove out of the former Street of the Sisters of the Sacrament. It stopped about a hundred metres away from you. The wind played with the billowing tents in the square and swept about piles of festival rubbish, skeins of streamers, yellowed newspapers, balloons, and bits of flags and banners.

"Attention!" said the officer in Russian, loudly exhaling.

Someone dressed in a camouflage jumpsuit and with a powerful megaphone slung around his chest appeared on top of the personnel carrier. And you heard his metallic, megaphone-distorted voice:

"Dear friends! Ladies and gentlemen! Brothers and sisters! I am happy to greet you at the beginning of the second day of our crazy drama. I am the festival's producer and director-in-chief, Pavlo Matsapura. I am sure that you have all enjoyed this rather sharp and unexpected joke, this happening in which you have become involuntary participants. I hope that none of you feels offended or hurt. Surprises were, after all, promised in the program. In two hours' time you are invited to come to the festival market. You may now fall out and continue amusing yourselves. The mass scenes were performed by the actors of the Youth and Experimental Theatres. Let us thank them for their accomplished performances with a round of enthusiastic applause!"

And all of you who stood with your backs to the sun began to clap madly, you clapped and could not stop, your hands began to hurt and still you did not stop, while the officers and the soldiers bowed in all directions.

Matsapura leapt down from the vehicle and, bowing in response to the applause and calls of "bravo!" headed in your direction. He was simply a genius, he shone, his glasses shone, his teeth, his boots shone. He recognized you from afar, waved, and trotted towards you.

"Well, what do you think?" he asked, embracing and kissing all of them, especially Marta.

"Ace," said Khoma.

"You've no idea how much all this cost—the machine guns, the vehicles, ten crates of blank cartridges—and the amount of running around I had to do to get it all approved, the sponsors helped, but I had to fight for everything myself, well, fortunately everything went without a hitch, it's great you turned up, there are all sorts of things still to come …"

"It suits you," Martofliak interrupted him.

"What, the paratrooper's uniform?" asked Matsapura.

"And altogether you're a great guy," said Hryts.

"So lend us three hundred," said Khoma.

"And give us a smoke," demanded Nemyrych.

Martofliak let go of his wife's hand.

"Shall we do some drinking later today?" he asked.

"Yes, but don't forget, your poetry evening's at eight," said Matsapura, taking off his glasses and cleaning them with his handkerchief. "So you'll have to recite your poems, lads."

September–October 1990

Notes

1. Sashko (diminutive for Oleksandr) and Viktor: Oleksandr Irvanets (b. 1961) and Viktor Neborak (b. 1961) of the Bu-Ba-Bu writers' group.
2. Literally, Devilsburg.
3. A major city in western Ukraine and an early and energetic centre of the national revival of the second half of the 1980s.
4. The blue-and-yellow flag of the Ukrainian People's Republic of 1918–20 was prohibited under Soviet rule. It attained great popularity in 1989–90, and in 1991 it became the national flag of newly independent Ukraine.
5. A Ukrainian military formation in the armed forces of Austria-Hungary during the First World War. It subsequently played a major role in the wars to defend Ukrainian independence in 1918–21. Folklore associated with the Sich Riflemen, especially their songs, was popular among émigré Ukrainians and enjoyed a boom in Ukraine in the late 1980s.
6. This name is familiar to Ukrainian readers from the first literary work in vernacular Ukrainian, Ivan Kotliarevsky's *Eneida* (1798–1842), a parody on Virgil's *Aeneid*. The first book of Kotliarevsky's mock epic was published without his consent by Maksym Parpura in St. Petersburg. Kotliarevsky responded by including in the third book, published in 1808, a portrait of "a certain Matsapura" undergoing torment in Hades for breaching copyright and "profiting from the property of others." The notes to the scholarly edition of Kotliarevsky remark that Pavlo Matsapura, "as evidenced by a decree of the Nizhyn regimental chancery in 1740, distinguished himself by terrible crimes, including 'the devouring of human flesh and other godless malfeasances.'" Andrukhovych uses this gloss as an epigraph to his poem "Pavlo Matsapura, Criminal" (1989), in which he offers a characteristically ambivalent interpretation of the felon.
7. A popular card game.
8. "Acceleration" (*uskorenie*): one of the slogans of the early Gorbachev period, alongside "openness" (*glasnost*) and "restructuring" (*perestroika*).
9. Refrain of the Sich Riflemen's song, "Mr. Lieutenant, have you heard ..."
10. Nagorno-Karabakh, an Armenian Christian enclave within largely Muslim Azerbaijan. In 1988 it became the object of claims by neighbouring Armenia and the scene of armed conflict between the two countries. Fergana, a city in Uzbekistan, was in 1990 and later years the scene of violence between resurgent Muslim and secular post-Communist power groups. Both locations symbolize

the ethnic and religious conflicts that erupted as Soviet central authority waned on the eve of the fall of the USSR in 1991.

11. A Soviet organization for the ideological and social indoctrination of young children in the spirit of Communism, especially through leisure and outdoor activities. It was similar to the scouting movements in Western countries.

12. A Hungarian bus widely regarded as superior to its Soviet counterparts.

13. In Slavic fairy tales, the happy end frequently includes the motif of the male and female heroes dying on the same day after a long life together.

14. The Communist Youth League.

15. The acronym of *Spilka nezalezhnoi ukrainskoi molodi* (Association of Independent Ukrainian Youth), a patriotic organization founded in the late 1980s.

16. The colours of the Ukrainian nationalist movement since 1929. They were worn as a sign of radical anti-Soviet sentiment in the late 1980s.

17. There is no canton with that name in Switzerland. Bayonne is a city in south-western France.

18. A Ukrainian ethnographic group indigenous to the Carpathians that is renowned for its colourful folklore and folkways.

19. Bohdan-Ihor Antonych (1909–37), a Ukrainian lyric poet of remarkable originality beloved by Ukrainian émigré modernist poets (especially the New York Group) and, since the 1960s, in Ukraine. Ivan Malkovych (b. 1961), a poet, did much to popularize Antonych through a children's edition of his poems in the early 1990s.

20. The Zaporozhian Cossacks were an autonomous Ukrainian warrior society noted for its warlike customs and picturesque appearance. They lived in the steppes below the Dnieper Rapids from the sixteenth century until they were dispersed by Russian imperial forces in 1775.

21. "Recreations" *(rekreatsii* or *rekreantsii)* were associated with students of the Kyiv Mohyla Academy in the eighteenth century. They took place outside the city walls, and their program included dramatic and poetic performances and rhetorical competitions.

22. A line from Kotliarevsky's *Eneida*.

23. The name of a sadistic member of a revolutionary tribunal in Mykola Khvylovy's short story "I (A Romantic Etude)" (1924).

24. Volodymyr Kaufman and Yurii (Iurii) Kokh are graphic artists and illustrators closely associated with Andrukhovych and the Bu-Ba-Bu group.

25. Mykola Nahnybida (1911–85), a Ukrainian poet and prose writer noted for his strict adherence to officially prescribed styles and themes.

26. A café in the building of the Writers Union of Ukraine in Kyiv, named for the hero of Kotliarevsky's *Eneida*. It is decorated with murals depicting scenes from the mock epic.

27. An official Soviet organization for cultivating relations with Ukrainians abroad and promoting Soviet achievements. It was widely spurned by Ukrainian émigrés for its links to the Soviet regime and its propaganda efforts.

28. Vitalii Korotych (b. 1936), a physician who became prominent as a Ukrainian poet in the 1960s. After the Chornobyl disaster in 1986 he moved to Moscow, where, as a personal friend of Gorbachev and the chief editor of the magazine *Ogonek*, he came to be regarded as one of the leading promoters of *glasnost*.

29. Cesare Lombroso (1836–1909), an Italian criminologist whose interests centred on the relation between mental and physical disorders.

30. The official emblem of the Ukrainian People's Republic (1918–20) and post-Soviet Ukraine. It was proscribed in the USSR.

31. A city in Kazakhstan that grew rapidly during and after the Second World War as a consequence of the relocation of many Soviet industries there during the war.

32. The poem "Vesnianka do snu" (Spring Lullaby), of which this is the first strophe, did, in fact, appear in Andrukhovych's first collection, *Nebo i ploshchi* (Sky and Squares) (Kyiv, 1985).

33. Francis Ferdinand (1863–1914), the Austrian archduke whose assassination was the immediate cause of the First World War.

34. Sergei Esenin (1895–1925), a Russian poet who was extremely popular in his lifetime and from the late 1950s onward.

35. *Knyha Leva* (1936), the largest of Antonych's collections, which included his philosophical lyrics.

36. Probably Stepan Bandera (1909–59), the Ukrainian nationalist leader most demonized in postwar Soviet propaganda. He was assassinated in Munich by a Soviet agent.

37. Lancers in the Polish and German cavalry.

38. Blind itinerant minstrels in Ukraine from the Middle Ages to the twentieth century. Many of them perished during the Stalinist terror of the 1930s.

39. Cossacks in the personal bodyguard of the hetmans (see note 45).

40. A military caste that ruled in Egypt from the thirteenth to the early nineteenth century.

41. The elite guard of the Ottoman Sultan drawn from indoctrinated Christian children captured in Slavic lands.

42. In Ukrainian rituals of the Christmas cycle, young men and girls elected as the central figures of costumed and masked groups that went carolling from house to house on St. Melanie's Day (New Year's Eve).

43. A synonym for Jews.

44. Nomads active on Ukrainian territory between 250 b.c. and a.d. 250. In the late seventeenth and the eighteenth centuries many members of the Polish aristocracy believed that they were descended from the Sarmatians.

45. A Hutsul alpenhorn used mainly for ritual purposes.

46. The elected rulers of the Ukrainian Cossack state in the seventeenth and eighteenth centuries.

47. The Mochemordy, a humorously conceived society of Ukrainian patriots in the 1840s.

48. A Christian sect influenced by Manichaeism, which originated in Armenia in the seventh century. Andrukhovych includes them for the sake of juxtaposing like-sounding words to create incongruous combinations: *Pavlykiany* (Paulicians) and *Paviany* (Baboons).

49. The daughters of Danaus, king of Argos, who murdered their husbands on their wedding night and were condemned eternally to fill sieve-like vessels with water.

50. A small ethnic group in the Russian Far East.

51. A small ethnic group living in the Amur valley and on Sakhalin Island in the Russian Far East.

52. Mikhail Lomonosov (1711–65), a pioneering Russian scientist and writer.

53. Today (German).

54. Very bad (German).

55. For example (German).

56. The official greeting that members of the Organization of Ukrainian Nationalists exchange.

57. A Hutsul men's dance.

58. Pavlo Polubotok (1660–1724), the acting hetman of Russian-dominated eastern Ukraine (1722–24), was said to have deposited a barrel of gold with the Bank of England. Speculation as to how much the capital might be worth with accrued interest engaged the Ukrainian press in the early 1990s. The bank disclaimed knowledge of the deposit.

59. "Who's she with now, who's kissing her fingers": a quotation from a popular song by the Russian poet Aleksandr Vertinsky.

60. "Music is moving architecture": a play on Goethe's words, "I have found among my papers a sheet in which I call architecture frozen music" (1829).

61. A play on Lenin's well-known tag, "Communism is Soviet power plus electrification of the whole country."

62. An inversion of the line "In unity is the strength of the people," from the hymn "O God, Hear Our Entreaties," which was popular in western Ukraine and the Ukrainian diaspora.

63. An inversion of the title of a film popular in the USSR in the 1970s, *This Sweet Word Is Freedom*.

64. Cf. "I disapprove of what you say, but I will defend to the death your right to say it," attributed to Voltaire.

65. Dmytro Dontsov (1883–1973), an ideologue of radical Ukrainian integral nationalism before the Second World War, regarded by Soviet officialdom as a major ideological enemy.

66. Ivan Bohun (d. 1664), a Cossack colonel renowned for his military prowess.

67. Ivan Mazepa (1639–1709), the hetman of Eastern Ukraine from 1687, who was demonized in the Russian Empire and the USSR. He has been glorified since the late 1980s for his attempt to restore Ukrainian independence. His exploits as a youth inspired numerous Romantic poets, most notably Byron.

68. A heavily industrialized, mainly Russian-speaking mining region in Eastern Ukraine.

69. NKVD (Russian: *Narodnyi kommissariat vnutrennikh del*), the People's Commissariat for Internal Affairs, Stalin's dreaded secret police.

70. Holders of state pensions for special service to the Soviet Party-state apparat.

71. Sofiia Rotaru, a pop singer from Bukovyna in western Ukraine, who has recorded in Ukrainian, Russian, and Romanian.

72. A refrain from a song by Sofiia Rotaru.

73. Rainer Maria Rilke (1875–1926) and Heinrich Heine (1797–1856), German poets mentioned here for the sake of the prewar west Ukrainian inflection of their surnames, which sounds quaint to the inhabitants of contemporary Ukraine.

74. Mykola Kholodny (b. 1939), a Ukrainian dissident poet highly regarded in the 1960s and imprisoned during the 1972 purge of Ukrainian intellectuals.

75. A card game of great complexity.

76. Beelzebub: the prince of devils in the Gospels; Lucifer: in Christian tradition, the name of Satan before his fall; Iblis: the name of the devil in the Koran; Asmodeus: in the Old Testament, the Talmud, and the apocrypha, an evil spirit and chief of all demons; Zoroaster: a reformer of the religion of ancient Iran in the late seventh and early sixth century B.C., subsequently identified in Western tradition as an archheretic and magician; Basavriuk: in Nikolai Gogol's *Evenings on a Farm Near Dikanka* (1831), the devil in human form. Margadon and Gynekhoshe are unknown to the annotator, as is any Calvin other than the reformer (1509–64).

77. An allusion to the inscription on the gravestone of the itinerant Ukrainian philosopher Hryhorii Skovoroda (1722–94), "The world chased me but did not catch me."

78. One of the crimes for which the historical Matsapura was executed (see note 6).

79. A term popularized by *Rozstriliane vidrodzhennia* (The Executed Renaissance), ed. Iurii Lavrinenko (Paris, 1959), an influential anthology of the works of Ukrainian writers executed or silenced under Stalinist rule in the late 1920s and 1930s.